ONE HALF-BREATH AT A TIME

Discover how to turn stress and anxiety into calm ease, productive power, and joy with Breath-Centered Practices

---

JOSEPH R. ROBERSON

Paper Tiger Press

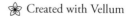

This book is dedicated to my grandson, Asher Tomás Roberson.

Foreword

I've been teaching yoga for 45 years and have known Joe for at least 25 years of those. I first met Joe in the early 90s when he attended one of my workshops, soon after the publication of my second book. Since that time, we've shared in each other's journeys. Joe is the quintessential renaissance man. He's a painter, writer, consummate yogi, and true seeker. In 2008, for instance, while Ana and I were leading a Kundalini Yoga workshop at Omega Institute in New York, Joe was attending a Visionary Artist Intensive led by Alex and Allyson Grey.

Joe has truly embodied these teachings in his lifetime journey. Joseph has a driving passion to get at the truth of things. His interest in yoga led him on a quest to clarify for himself the essence of the priceless teachings of yoga. He has studied in India and for most of his adult life has immersed himself in committed yogic practice. Joe and I are kindred spirits who are not afraid to do an end-run around dogma to arrive at what's real and true.

I was living in New York City, in Lower Manhattan, when 9/11 happened. I was scheduled to teach a workshop for Joe in Maryland, but I felt an obligation to stay in New York and do volunteer work. Joe agreed, without hesitation. Only later did I learn he had to intercede on my behalf with the owner of the studio, who was furious and vowed never to book us ever again.

These days, mainstream medicine has a medication for every syndrome and a syndrome for every tingle. This is not a sustainable approach. We all need to get back to basics to restore some sanity to the proceedings—and what could be more doable than something we're already doing, namely breathing!

It may be what us yogis have long suspected: Breath is the best medicine of all. The Saints and Sages of the Ages in their wisdom knew that desperate times called for desperate measures and that nothing is more immediate, direct, powerful, and purifying than conscious breathing.

Joe's approach in this book is definitely a breath of fresh air. What Ana and I especially appreciate about Joe's teaching and writing is that he doesn't succumb to "yoga speak;" he shares his personal journey in a way that is truly authentic. In his Prologue, Joe describes his harrowing experience of being robbed at gunpoint; he attributes his survival that day to his decades of breath-centered practices, as provided in this book. His writing is creative, accurate, inspired, and fun; he brings an artistic vision to his path and practice that perfectly complements his commitment to scientific rigor.

Based on our experience, we can guarantee that if you make a commitment to the methods Joe shares, you will be healthier, happier, more creative, more courageous, more expansive, and more energized. May Joe's great work, a veritable breath bible, be the resonator that oscillates this important message around the world.

-Ravi Singh and Ana Brett, authors of *The Kundalini Yoga Book*
- *Life in the Vast Lane*

Read This First

Breathwork is powerful medicine. Its effectiveness as a natural therapeutic modality has been esteemed since ancient times. Some of these are beyond the scope of this book, which for the most part, is limited to easy, simple, and harmless practices anyone can incorporate into their daily life.

If you have a history of trauma, anxiety, depression, panic attacks—or any other mental health problems—please consult with a qualified professional before you attempt any of these practices.

If, on the other hand, you do not have any serious psychological or physical health issues, feel free to jump right in. If you are so inclined, proceed straight to Part 4, Getting Started With Breath-Centered Practices, and begin immediately. You can always read the other parts at your leisure, as your interest dictates.

Medical Disclaimer

The information you are being provided by this author—whether contained within this book or via URL links to websites, courses, programs, products, and services—is for educational and informational purposes only. All content is made available to you as a self-help tool for your own use. It is not intended to take the place of professional medical help.

Legal Stuff

Although every reasonable effort has been taken to ensure the accuracy of all information presented herein by this author, be advised that this book may inadvertently contain inaccuracies or typographical errors. Every effort has been made to present you with the most accurate, up-to-date information, but because the nature of scientific research, technology, and best practices are constantly evolving, I cannot be held responsible for the accuracy of said information.

Additionally, this author cannot be held responsible for the views, opinions, or accuracy of facts referenced within this book, nor those found on referenced or linked websites, courses, programs, products or services, whether or not they belong to this author.

By using my Website, Programs, Products and Services you implicitly signify your agreement to all parts of the above disclaimer. If you have any questions about this disclaimer, please contact the author.

Contents

Part Seven
RESOURCES

Prologue

I love taking these long walks. Especially when I have the luxury of staying out as long as I want, with no pressure, no deadline, no certain time I have to be back. The best walks, for me, are the ones where I just keep walking and walking and walking until everything leaves my head–until my brain stops and everything gets quiet. Until there is only walking. Until there is only witnessing. Long before I learned the formal Buddhist walking meditation technique of *Vipassana* in Thailand, I loved them. I discovered that walking was an effortless way to fall into meditation.

I'm almost home now. My front door is just around the corner. I stop walking. I can't go in, I think to myself, until I've figured out tomorrow's presentation for yoga teacher training. I need to land on a way to explain what the three *Gunas* are.

Since my best ideas usually come to me during meditation, I decide to practice what I now call *Coherence Walking*, which is basically *Vipassana* combined with *Coherent Breathing*^{TM1}. Like this:

in-step, *hale*-step, *three*-step, *four*-step, *five*-step, *six*-step,

ex-step, *hale*-step, *three*-step, *four*-step, *five*-step, *six*-step

This is one of my favorites. Waiting for the breath, moving from breath's lead, is usually all it takes to rein in my runaway mind. I've done it so many times over so many years that it's almost automatic. Plus, it's so simple, so easy to do.

But not today.

Determined to break through this noise, this brain turbulence, and emerge in the clear sky that lies at the center of my little storm, I persist. I begin again. I decide not to stop until all I'm doing is breathing and walking. Until I am present.

I'm moving much slower now, like a video in slow motion. Frame by frame. Instead of six steps for one half-breath, now it's one foot rising for the inhale and then lowering with the exhale. It's a good thing Hollins Street is empty, because anybody who sees me do this might think I'm strung out on heroin. Or crazy. Or both.

Inquiry Question: Is my breathing shallow or deep as I read these words?

I don't have the foggiest idea how long this went on until I said to myself mid-step: *Now you know why you kept staring at Winnie, Tigger, and Eeyore yesterday in the Disney Store. They're the three gunas! Winnie, Tigger, and Eeyore are the perfect avatars to represent the balanced alternations between contraction and expansion, between acceptance, change, and the wisdom to choose the right response. Winnie is sattva, Tigger is rajas, and Eeyore is tamas! Of course! Bingo!*

Coming back to my surroundings now, I'm surprised by how

dark everything has become. Twilight is slipping quickly into night.

How long ago did I leave the house? How long have I been lost in my meditation? Oh yeah, today is fall-back Sunday. Totally forgot to change my clock. Hey, there's the first star! Or is that a planet — Venus? Now that cup of Yogi Tea sounds perfect.

A street light on the other side of Hollins Street flickers and flashes to blink itself awake. Several more stars twinkle overhead.

A gun barrel presses cold and hard into my cheek. A tiny spot of light blinks on and off the end of the barrel reflected from the streetlight. I look up to see who's holding the gun but all I can make out is a blank silhouette against the glare.

It barks:

Gimme your money!

The silhouette speaks with a boy's voice. And this voice sounds scared, which is not a good sign.

Hand it over, whitey. Or I'll give you a cap to go with that stupid hat!

To myself, I say, *Look him in the eye! And keep breathing! He can't know you're scared of him. Or the gun.* To the silhouette with the boyish voice, I say,

Just relax. Stay calm. It's gonna be okay, son.

Shut the fuck up! Where's the money, redneck?

I says to myself, says I, *Oops, wrong tone. He's gotta show you he's calling the shots here. Okay, Okay. Let's try again. But what's this? Oh crap!*

A second gun makes its presence known at my left earlobe. Instinctively, my head turns towards it only to be wrenched back by the silhouette's bark:

Eyes on me, motherfucker!

My eyes did not have a chance to focus, but yet I sensed something else going down behind assailant number two. All I could really see was a blur, but the wrenching of my gut told me all I needed to know: more reinforcements are sprinting up to join in the fun.

Inside my head, I hear, *You're fucked, Joe.*

But despite the quaking of my knees and the terror in my heart, my breathing rhythm remains unbroken. It's the only thing keeping me from freaking out.

Again, the silhouette barks:

I said, hand over the money! Where the fuck's your dough?

Ever so slowly, I reach up and slide the green Eagle Creek 'man purse' off my right shoulder as I reply,

It's in the front pocket.

Dangling it towards the silhouette, I proffer my final plea:

I don't care about the money. Just take it.

Jerking it away, he takes flight down Hollins Street, toward the Market, homies in tow. Bent over, gasping for air, I listen as their footfalls fade into the night.

The whole thing was over in 90 seconds flat, if that.

Question: Do you think my decades of breath-centered practices saved my life?

Introduction

While I can't prove it to you, I'm positive my relative calm throughout an armed robbery saved my life, and allowed me to escape without a scratch. In the hours and days after that incident, I replayed the scene over and over in my head. What would have happened had I freaked out or fought back or run or screamed? How would they have reacted if I insulted them? Did maintaining eye contact with my assailant's blank silhouette make a difference?

The only thing I was sure of was that my practices helped me steer the outcome. I am so lucky I fell in love with meditation, breathwork, and yoga at the age of fourteen.

Speaking of steering the outcome, consider what one San Diego police officer wrote in his evaluation after participating in a Resilience Training pilot program:

> Last week, I was in a situation in which a person squared off on me and started reaching in his jacket. I went to my breath and activated coherence and never felt anything but calm. As I noticed the sirens of my backup arriving, I realized my

heart was beating slowly. Every other time that has happened, I basically screamed for backup and it took me a whole day to calm down. When my captain got there, he said he thought I was kidding when I put out the call because I sounded so calm on the radio. He asked what I'd been doing differently. This stuff is for real. The knowledge that I can control my reactions is huge![1]

Are Breath-centered Practices for me?

Of all the methods I've seen [...] the most time effective and cost effective are breathing techniques. ... It literally makes use of something that's right under your nose, it requires no equipment, and it's free.

Andrew Weil, M.D.

There are only two ways to reduce stress: eliminate the cause or increase capacity. Reducing or eliminating stress is an attractive option for many people, but who really wants to give up everything modern life makes possible? I say the better solution is to increase our capacity! Only by increasing your capacity can you successfully take on additional stress, be it a new job, getting married, raising children, or weathering an unforeseen crisis. If you want to thrive, breath-centered practices will be of tremendous help; not only will they help you manage whatever stress you have now, but they also increase your ability to perform under the increased levels of stress that come with success.

Are you worried about how you'll find the time to do these practices? Or do you think it selfish to indulge in 'me time'? Allow me to dispel those misunderstandings right now. The truth is, breathwork changes everything you do. When you practice first thing in the morning, it especially changes how your day unfolds. You will be less reactive. More patient. A better listener. A better performer. A better friend, spouse, parent, child. Maybe even a better boss.

You—and everyone you interact with—will be glad you did.

I have studied, practiced, and taught each one of these techniques. Over the years I have tweaked, altered, and customized them–and occasionally come up with something new. But you can rest assured that every technique is grounded in tradition; many have been studied by eminent researchers in the field, such as Dan Siegel, Sat Bir Khalsa, and Shirley Telles. I've included their work where needed. At the same time, I have limited the number of citations to avoid turning this introductory book into an academic tome.

Without a doubt, the most heartening evidence for the power of these techniques I have found comes from their use as a treatment for post-traumatic stress syndrome, or PTSD. Later on, you'll learn more about that. This book is not about treating trauma, however. The purpose of this book is to provide tools for garden-variety stress, not major illness.

Breath-centered practices bring you home, back to the place you've been too busy to visit–your living, breathing body. From there, the sky's the limit: they can take you to blissful states as high as the stars. I experienced this after a breath intensive in India. I call it my mountaintop experience. I can only describe it with paltry words such as bliss, the Garden of Eden, and the peace that surpasses understanding.

Benefits

- Resilience
- Increased capacity for stress
- Better sleep
- Better communication
- Increased focus and concentration
- More energy
- Effortless weight loss
- Sense of calm serenity
- More courage
- Access to intuition and innate wisdom

Is This Book For You?

Let me say the main thing right here, right now: your greatest resource for having more energy, vitality, enjoyment, and productivity is not inside these pages.

Ready for the good news?

You already have it. Your easiest, most direct access to increased vitality, productivity, and happiness has been right here under your nose the whole time you've been searching for it! Breath-centered practices, as you will soon discover, are simple tools, techniques, and practices with which you will access them. They are simple, easy to learn, and, you'll be happy to know, easy to incorporate into a busy lifestyle.

Whether the crisis at hand is a matter of life and death or a matter of surviving your daily commute, breath-centered practices work. You don't have to be on the front lines—you needn't be a soldier or police officer—to suffer the ill effects of stress. But you can be sure of one thing: if the military believes breath-centered practices are effective, they must work. And if they help in life-and-death situations, you can be sure they can help you perform better.

Breathing for many, if not most, of us is 'invisible': what I mean is that breathing tends to be unconscious and unappreciated. In this book, you will discover how your own breathing can become a barometer, a tool, a companion, a mystery, and a miracle. You will learn several powerful, yet simple and easy, practices to stimulate, calm, and balance your energy, mood, and mind.

This book is for you if:

- You are looking for a natural, holistic, and healthy way to manage stress, anxiety, insomnia, or depression
- You want to take charge of your own health and well-being; you want to cultivate greater health, vitality, and resilience
- You are seeking spiritual growth and transformation, in order to manifest your greatest potential
- You are looking for a better way to increase your productivity, whether in your studies or your job
- You find yourself unable to concentrate and you want to sharpen your focus, stay on task, on track—you want to get more done with less anxiety
- You are a teacher, a mental health professional, a caregiver, parent, therapist, doctor, coach, or a mentor, and you are looking for new ways to help those you serve

Why One Half-Breath?

Speaking of the present moment, are you wondering why the title is "One Half-Breath At A Time" instead of "One Breath At A Time"? The reason is simple. According to Daniel N. Stern, M.D., author of *The Present Moment in Psychotherapy and Everyday Life*, what we call 'the present moment' lasts a mere three to five seconds. Breathing slowly, at a rate of six times per minute, means each inhale and each exhale lasts approximately five seconds. Thus, one half-breath equals one moment of now. I would argue that there is no present moment at all, no *now*, any time you breathe faster than eight or 10 breaths per minute. You're alive, obviously. You may be productive and efficient. But you are not present in it. In short, your only access to optimum focus, productivity, vitality, power, intimacy, and *presence* lies within this half-breath, and this half-breath alone.

Inquiry Question: Is my breathing stress-free or stressed out? In this moment, is my breathing smooth and rhythmic—or is it jerky and ragged? In this right-here, right-now half-breath, effortless and easy—or is it, instead, effortful and uneasy?

While you're reading this book, and especially as you're doing the exercises and inquiries, allow yourself space to do what you're doing. Be present. For that time span, those moments you spend focused on your breathing, indulge yourself in the simple pleasure of rhythm. The simple act of turning one's attention onto the cyclical pattern of breathing can be profoundly calming. It only takes two or three cycles for a feeling of pleasure to arise, for

> Rhythm is one of the most powerful of
>   pleasures, and when we feel a pleasurable
>   rhythm we hope it will continue. When it

does, it grows sweeter. When it becomes
reliable, we are in a kind of body-heaven.

-Mary Oliver

You might need to spend time getting more acquainted with
your own breathing—develop greater sensitivity towards it—
before that's even possible,. That's the purpose of spending time
practicing the deep breath inquiry, as well as cultivating the tiny
habit of mindfulness of how you breathe in different situations
outside of formal practice.

Above all, start enjoying breathing a little more. Just because
you can. Remind yourself often that the best things in life,
including this half-breath you're taking right now, are free.
Dormant joy and latent bliss exist nowhere else, only in this
inhale, only in this exhale. Don't miss it!

Breath-centered practices are so simple, in fact, there's no reason
not to start right now!

Your First Breath Practice (instructions)

1. Inhale slow and deep
2. Hold the air inside for three to eight seconds
3. Exhale even more slowly than you inhaled through your
   mouth
4. Allow the air to flow out as you relax your jaw, lips –
   every part of your face
5. Inhale again, even slower and deeper
6. Hold it a little longer this time to absorb all that oxygen,
   all that life energy you inspired!
7. Exhale as before but really draw it out long and slow as
   you relax your entire body, heart, and mind.

Imagine the Difference

Question: What difference would it make–to you, but also to those you love and cherish–if you knew how to:

- Defuse stress and anxiety simply by changing your breathing
- Respond calmly rather than react in unpleasant situations
- Summon hidden reserves of energy, stamina, and courage with one quick and easy breathing trick
- Relax deeply
- Sleep better - and wake up restored
- Access deep reserves of creativity, serenity, and wisdom
- Increase your resilience
- Shake off stress or even learn to turn it into a renewable energy source
- Be more accepting, patient, and tolerant
- Spend more moments during your day feeling calm, happy, even joyous for no reason
- Uncover, or recover, your true nature: bliss!

While you may not be able to establish and sustain an ambitious, formal home practice initially, that's not a problem. I'll show you a simple and effective method for creating your first breath habit. Before you know it, you will reap dividends far greater than your investment. The effects grow quickly, snowballing by the power of compound interest!

You—and everyone you interact with—will be glad you did.

DISTRESS CALL

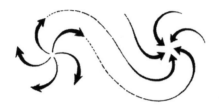

ONE

VUCA-Dukkha, Distress-Disease

There's a new, urgent need to solve the growing incidence of diseases caused by chronic stress. The search is on for a solution that does not involve drugs or surgery. Is there such a thing? Breath-centered practices are effective because they address the root of the problem; instead of masking symptoms, they address the cause-and-effect sequence:

VUCA-Dukkha, Distress-Disease

The U.S. Centers for Disease Control (CDC) identifies chronic diseases as responsible for seven of 10 deaths each year, and treating people with chronic diseases accounts for most of our nation's healthcare costs.

Hypertension (chronically elevated blood pressure) is one of the fastest-growing diseases. Over 50% of Medicare subscribers suffer from high blood pressure; 25% suffer more advanced stages of heart disease. The cost? Over $100 billion annually.

Until recently, hypertension was thought of as a problem of the affluent, of city dwellers living in the fast lane. Not anymore. The findings of The Lancet's study of global health trends, published on November 15, 2016, are sobering:

> The number of adults with raised blood pressure increased from 594 million in 1975 to 1.13 billion in 2015, with the increase largely in low-income and middle-income countries.

Very few of those 1.13 billion people can afford expensive treatments, even if they had access to them. What is urgently needed is a low-cost alternative, along the lines of the cheap water purification innovations that hold such great promise toward providing drinking water in drought-stricken regions.

Is there such a thing?

TWO

VUCA

—————

Hold back the edges of your gowns, Ladies, we are going through hell.[1]

The U.S. Army War College coined the acronym VUCA to describe the volatility, uncertainty, complexity, and ambiguity the United States faced when the Cold War ended. Unpredictability replaced the stalemate of assured mutual destruction. What the War College got wrong was its assumption that a new and stable world order would emerge. What happened instead is the world we live in today, a world of ever-increasing volatility, uncertainty, complexity, and ambiguity.

The global crisis of lifestyle diseases is symptomatic of the world you and I live in today. Lifestyle diseases are the inevitable, logical outcome of ever-increasing VUCA. Anxiety, depression, insomnia, ADHD, diabetes, hypertension, opioid addiction, and all the rest of the lifestyle diseases are increasing in proportion to the increases in the number and severity of wildfires, hurricanes, mass shootings, and terrorist attacks. All you need do is run down the list. For example, let's look just at recent terrorist attacks. This week it's Charlottesville, Turku, and Barcelona. In recent weeks, there was Finsbury Park, London Bridge, Manchester. In the past year, New York, Paris, Brussels, Stockholm. And we all remember San Bernadino, the nightclub massacre in Fort Lauderdale, all those elementary school kids in Sandy Hook, Connecticut.

As Bob Dylan–Nobel laureate and sage of our age–points out, *everything is broken*!

While these diverse symptoms may seem unrelated because they appear in completely different realms, they are not.

Any threat, real or imaginary, triggers the stress response. The body reacts the same way to a threat to your ego as it does to actual danger to life and limb. We don't usually recognize how much tension we invest in simple activities such as talking or cooking, because we don't recognize the situation as stressful.

Stress disorders breathing in many ways. Stopping it abruptly is part and parcel of the fright, fight, or flight stress response. The stress you feel, that shows up in how you breathe, is not an isolated phenomena. Each time you breathe in you also take in the world around you. Breathing is one of the many ways you interact with and process your surroundings. The air is part of your diet, so to speak. And the news you consume, your daily media intake, is also part of your diet.

The Rising Cost of Living

Even if you don't consider yourself to be in business, you are in engaged, at this very moment, in the business of living. Every business has systems. Corporations have physical plant systems, production systems, management systems, financial systems, information systems, sales and marketing systems, packaging and distribution systems. The human body also has multiple systems: skeletal, muscular, respiratory, nervous, cardiovascular, digestive, social, cultural, religious, and so many more.

Regardless of whether we're talking about a business or a body, all the systems that go to make up the whole must work together in harmony to remain viable, much less to achieve long-term growth, success, and to manifest a vision. What happens to those systems under conditions of volatility, uncertainty, complexity, and ambiguity? If the systems are resilient, they process the increased stress successfully; if the systems lack resilience, they fail.

Trivia question: Who was the first of all the gods in Greek mythology?

Another day, another reorganization

To thrive in the new global economy you have to be adept at continuous—and self-directed—learning. You must be able to find, synthesize, and evaluate information from a wide variety of subjects and sources. Alvin Toffler predicted as much in 1970 when he wrote:

> The illiterate of the 21st century will not be those who cannot read and write, but those who cannot learn, unlearn, and relearn.[2]

Alvin Toffler

The days are gone when you could expect to work at one job at one company until retirement. Nowadays, most people change jobs, companies, even careers multiple times throughout their lives. They can no longer depend on the company to provide a safe and secure home away from home. Employers can no longer be depended upon to look after your best interests, like surrogate parents. Today, you're on your own. I hope you mind if I quote Bob Dylan again: *I haven't known peace and quiet for so long, I've forgotten what it's like!*

Question: Has VUCA arrived in your world? Has your life become chaotic–more volatile, more uncertain, more complex, more ambiguous? Does it make you confused and susceptible? Even gullible?

As the pace of technological progress accelerates, so does the volume of data, information, and knowledge. And then there's the data breaches, identity thefts, hackers, and mind manipulators. To nefarious marketers, terrorist organizations, and big players wielding sophisticated persuasive tools in the influence game, such as Cambridge Analytica, your mind is a bullseye target. They deploy military-grade analytics to send you precisely the right ad at precisely the right moment. The persuasion industry knows exactly how to manipulate your emotions, how to sway your decisions their way.

VUCA situations in daily life

- Job Pressure: coworker tension, bosses, work overload
- Money: loss of job, reduced retirement, medical expenses
- Health: health crisis, terminal or chronic illness
- Relationships: divorce, death of spouse, arguments with friends, loneliness
- Poor Nutrition: inadequate nutrition, caffeine, processed foods, refined sugars

- Media Overload: television, radio, internet, email, social networking
- Sleep Deprivation: inability to release adrenaline and other stress hormones

---

When Do I Hold My Breath? (instructions)

Question: I used to ask my students and private clients, "Do you hold your breath?" What I found intriguing was how many answered "No" initially only to change their answer after a week of self-observation. So, let me ask you what I ask all my students nowadays:

When do you hold your breath?

You can't change a habit if you're not even aware of it! You may be surprised and disconcerted to discover that you hold your breath in almost every conceivable situation.

Over the course of the week, make a mental note of the situations in which you engage in breath holding. Make your observations without reproach or disappointment. But if your inner critic chimes in, saying bad things about you, don't be surprised. Actually, I'll be surprised if you don't. This is every bit as important as your breathing pattern because your breathing pattern is affected by your thoughts and emotions. This exercise will shine a light on the moment-by-moment influences among thought, emotion, posture, and breath.

Common Places and Times to Investigate:

- While talking to _____ (your spouse, parent, child, boss, or a certain coworker)
- Driving

- Hurrying to get out the door
- Remembering an unpleasant event
- Fantasizing about _____
- Completing a task

Celebrate each time you catch yourself holding your breath! The more times you see it, the more aware you become.

It's not just the General and the CEO who need to learn how to navigate the fog and friction so prevalent under VUCA conditions. The problem is no longer confined to military campaigns, multinational corporations, and the like. Today, VUCA has trickled down and, with it, so has the need for a tool to effectively cope with its challenges. You and I—and most especially our children—need it, too.

Is there such a thing?

Trivia question answer: Chaos

THREE

Dukkha

Mr. Duffy lived a short distance from his body.[1]

James Joyce

Given all the different kinds of changes and disruptions we encounter nowadays, it's no surprise we experience more and more worry, confusion, anxiety, fear, and depression. How do we cope with it? More and more, we dissociate. And whenever we dissociate, we create suffering, we create what Buddha called *dukkha*.

Dukkha comes from the Pali language. It is formed by combining *du*, which means bad or worn (and therefore unserviceable), together with *kha*, which means an opening, hole, or aperture. Dukkha denotes the noise an ox cart with a worn out axle made, like the grinding noise my car made before I got the worn out wheel bearings replaced. When used in a Buddhist context, *dukkha* connotes anguish, the subjective, psychological 'inner noise' a person with a complaint makes.

Whenever we bitch and moan, be it silently or out loud, we express our experience of dukkha.

The Mind/Body Problem

> A person lives through two collateral histories, one comprising of what happens in and to the body, the other consisting of what happens in and to his mind [...] The events in the first history are events in the physical world, those in the second are events in the mental world.[2]

When you were born, you were whole, complete, and undivided. By the time you were old enough to write, you were not. How does this happen?

Part and parcel of the process of growing up is rejecting unsatisfactory, unsavory parts of oneself. We are born natural and then 'improved' by nurture, by parenting, schooling, religion, culture, and many other influences. Through the process of shaping the feral infant into a socialized human citizen, each of us develops a second, virtual nature. This improved, language-conditioned mental construct nearly always rejects and represses those uncivilized aspects—feral, animal—of our original nature.

The mind/body problem is a language problem—a problem with the mental process of mapping the terrain. A problem caused by a misfit between word and world. To think of ourselves as having a body rather than being a body makes perfect sense, in a pretzel-logic, neurotic sort of way. Pretzel logic aside, this bifurcation—saying my body—is ultimately nonsensical. Just as straight lines do not exist in nature, there is no sharp line dividing mind and body. Only in language do they exist as two separate things.

Dissociation

Pretending to be invisible at a social gathering to avoid speaking to someone is not dissociating. But if, while speaking to this person, you pretend to be listening while you're distracting yourself by thinking of who you can escape to, then you are dissociating. Understanding dissociation as natural and normal provides a new way to explain why so many of us deny the body's basic needs, such as for food and adequate sleep. Been there, done that. I lived on four to six hours of sleep throughout graduate school.

Mind/Body Dissociation

Distinguishing mind and body as two separate things is part of the work of creating mental maps. This process, in a nutshell, is the genesis of the so-called mind/body problem. Let's call a spade a spade, shall we? Let's call it what it really is: dissociation.

Dissociation comes in many forms, and are classified as primitive, more mature, and mature. But underlying each and every one is a natural and normal fear of dying. Like every other living creature, humans are hard-wired for survival. Woody Allen's oft-quoted quip, *I ain't afraid of dying, but I don't want to be there when it happens,* expresses what every living creature feels instinctively. And yet we, as a species, seem to have reached a mutual understanding between us not to admit to it—even to ourselves.

> Dissociation means, literally, 'not associating (with something or someone).' In psychology and psychiatry, dissociation is defined as "a disconnection between a person's thoughts, memories, feelings, actions, or sense of who he or she is. This is a normal process that everyone has experienced. Examples of mild, common dissociation include daydreaming, highway hypnosis, or "getting lost" in a book or movie, all of which involve "losing touch" with one's immediate surroundings.[3]

What we talk about, when we speak of dissociation, are things like neuroticism, repression, acting out, and regression. These are associated with the more extreme disconnection between mind, body, and behavior. Compensation, assertiveness, and sublimation (transforming unhealthy urges into healthy behavior) are not usually referred to as dissociation. But they are. Just like stress, 'dissociative defense mechanisms' are normal and natural—even essential. Here are a few examples of socially sanctioned dissociation, what we call focusing or selective attention:

- Sitting still in school and concentrating on what the teacher is saying instead of on the desire to play outside
- The altered state of rapture referred to as love at first sight
- Walking right past someone on the street even though she or he is speaking and/or gesturing to you
- Tuning out sounds and sights and smells as you concentrate on the task at hand
- Looking away from another person's gaze because she

or he is 'in my kitchen;' because your heart and soul
are seen

"...defense mechanisms are most often learned behaviors,
most of which we learned during childhood. That's a good
thing, because it means that, as an adult, you can choose to
learn some new behaviors and new defense mechanisms that
may be more beneficial to you in your life. Many
psychotherapists will help you work on these things, if you'd
like. But even becoming more aware of when you're using
one of the less primitive types of defense mechanisms above
can be helpful in identifying behaviors you'd like to reduce.[4]

Inquiry: Is it easy to concentrate on my breathing right now? If
not, what is interfering? Thinking about something that happened
in the past? Thinking about something that may happen at some
future time? Is there a specific place in my body where I feel it, a
specific sensation?

Buddha's Four Noble Truths

It's no surprise so many people say they experience the
symptoms of chronic stress: worry, sleep problems, fatigue,
confusion, anxiety, fear, depression, and many more. Buddha
called this mental anguish *dukkha*, the suffering we all feel when
the facts on the ground don't match our expectations for how
life should be.

The Four Noble Truths offer a diagnosis, prognosis, and remedy
for human suffering. According to the Buddhist tradition,
Gautam Buddha taught the noble truths during his first
teaching, after attaining full awakening and liberation from
rebirth. Like any good physician or healer, Buddha followed the
standard doctor/patient consultation template:

1. Analyze the patient's symptoms
2. Identify the cause
3. Recommend the best course of treatment
4. Provide treatment if possible

Let's unpack each one.

First Noble Truth

> Now this, bhikkhus, is the first noble truth: birth is pain, aging is pain, illness is pain, death is pain. Union with what is painful is suffering; separation from what pleases is suffering; not getting what one wants is suffering.
>
> Buddha

Although many translations use suffering throughout this passage, I have replaced some with pain. It is vital that we have a clear definition of terms with which to distinguish between a fact and what we say about it.

Nobody wants to experience aches and pains, regrets, old age, sickness, death. Yet, as we all know, they are as unavoidable as taxes. You and I—and every other creature who has lived, is living, or will ever live—will experience discomfort, pain, hurt, sickness, and death. Those are the facts of life. The birds and the bees. But humans are not like other creatures. Humans expect —demand, even—that daily life *not* be volatile, uncertain, complex, or ambiguous. I scream, you scream, we all scream, "I want stability, certainty, simple living, and clarity. No VUCA!"

To my mind, Buddha was simply pointing out the fact that stress, discomfort, pain, and death are not optional. Life's a beach some days and a bitch other days. And no one gets out alive.

Second Noble Truth

> Now this, bhikkhus, is the noble truth of the origin of suffering: it is this craving which leads to re-becoming, accompanied by delight and lust, seeking delight here and there; that is, craving for sensual pleasures, craving for becoming, craving for dis-becoming.
>
> Buddha

Buddha's second lesson is that we create our own suffering. Dukkha is the suffering we experience whenever reality doesn't conform to our mental picture, when the facts don't match our desire, when the map does not match the landscape. Buddha was not talking about life's curves and twists, ups and downs, trials and tribulations. Dukkha is caused by what we say about a fact, not by the fact itself.

You cause your own dukkha by confusing a physical feature of the roadway with a judgement about it, such as when you label a pothole a pain in the ass. Dukkha is the squeak you make inside your own wheelhouse, the noisy complaints inside your head. We call it anguish, suffering, anxiety, depression, or simply mental and emotional distress; Buddha calls it clinging.

What is more—your desire, or the facts?[5]

-Van Morrison

Humans desire a road that is smooth and straight. So, when it's not, we bitch and moan, complaining about potholes and traffic jams and speeding tickets. Or we dream about a new car that would provide a safe, uneventful, air-cushioned journey.

Not that wanting is bad. Not that striving to improve the road is bad. Just that some things can and should be changed, while others should be accepted as they are. Railing against what you cannot change is folly. Wisdom is choosing when to accept and when not to accept. That's all.

You create stress, suffering, and dukkha every time you say, whether silently, to yourself or to another, that something shouldn't be the way it is. The mismatch between what is and what 'should be' is the bad fit between axle and axle-hole. Expecting life to be a smooth journey, free of discomfort and displeasure, free of VUCA, creates dukkha. You create your own world of dukkha when your inner critic rails against what is.

This is the root cause of chronic stress. It's these internally generated stimuli, these predictions, that trigger the stress response, not external stimuli coming from outside the body. Chronic stress typically results from the same prediction being generated repeatedly, over and over and over and over like a broken record. Buddha described it as being stung to death by a single bee sting.

Third Noble Truth

> Now this, bhikkhus, is the noble truth of the cessation of suffering: it is the remainder-less fading away and cessation of that same craving, the giving up and relinquishing of it, freedom from it, non-reliance on it.
>
> -Buddha

Is there any hope for a smooth highway—or should I accept the potholes? Is the pursuit of happiness nothing more than a nefarious lie to get me to work more, spend more—to be a gullible fool?

Every form of anxiety, from the subliminal, universally

repressed, fear of death we all walk around avoiding all the way up to the daytime nightmare of PTSD, is an urge to escape.

What, exactly, do we want to escape from? Feelings, those murky, roiling floodwaters from below—from our own body! And where do we escape to? Up the stairs to the private room inside our mind. In short, we escape by dissociating.

So the answer is to give up trying to escape. Instead, be with your anxiety. Look it right in the eye. Observe yourself. Do you stop breathing when you feel distressed? Just note the facts, as a scientific observer observing someone else. Be curious. Be a social scientist, but one who studies himself. Know thyself!

In short, discomfort, pain, and death are unavoidable. But suffering is optional. As I understand it, the third noble truth says, in essence, that the way out is in. The only way to escape it is to stop trying to escape!

Drop That Dukkha! (instructions)

I learned this from Dan Brule, author of *Just Breathe!*, during a week-long conference at Kripalu, called *Breath Immersion: From Science to Samadhi*, in 2015. He calls it the Drop It Technique. Not only is this a simple technique, it's also fun! All you do is:

1. Inhale as slowly and deeply as comfortable. Hold it as long as is comfortable – without straining!
2. When you're ready to exhale, do so by releasing all tension from your head, neck, and shoulders – but especially your jaw muscles. That's where stress and anger collects.
3. Allow yourself to breathe a sigh of relief by allowing this exhale its voice; allow yourself a deliciously drawn-out let-go that sounds something like aaaaaaahhh…

4. When you finish, pause. Relax a moment.

Notice how taking such a simple, easy, and short 'breath break' changes how you feel. Enjoy how good it feels to breathe intentionally, how good it is to take a moment to 'smell the roses,' how good it feels to create this present moment, one half-breath at a time. Celebrate your first step toward a better quality of living. As you can already tell, a better quality of life is always available right here under your nose.

Fourth Noble Truth

> Now this, bhikkhus, is the noble truth of the way leading to the cessation of suffering: it is this noble eightfold path; that is, right view, right intention, right speech, right action, right livelihood, right effort, right mindfulness, right concentration.
>
> Buddha

There is a cure for anxiety, depression, insomnia and all the other manifestations of chronic stress. *Yee-ha!* To end suffering, Buddha says, just follow this simple recipe. To enjoy more health, wellness, vitality, and joy, cultivate these eight habits.

Breath-centered practices, as presented here in the following pages, incorporate all eight habits Buddha recommends. May they be, for you, just what the doctor ordered!

If it's true what they say, that the quality of this breath you are breathing right now is a measure of your quality of life, then you're already on your way!

FOUR

Distress

In physics, stress is the condition existing in elastic material when the strain of an external force acts upon it. Had my English been better at the time, I would have called my phenomenon the "strain syndrome," and that which causes it, "stress." However, I did not realize the difference. By the time I did, the word "stress" had become too generally accepted in medicine to make a change, so I had to invent the term "stressor," now used to describe the agent that causes physiologic stress. -Hans Selye[1]

U p to this point, we have examined the causes of stress, both external and internal,—VUCA and dukkha. In this chapter, we examine the stress response within the body. But what, exactly, are we talking about?

Chemistry or character?

The debate about stress—its causes and cures—has been raging since at least the time of Galen of Pergamon (129-200 A.D.), a Greek physician who served the Roman Empire.

Christianity had long taught that stress, what it called sloth and acedia (apathy, listlessness), stems from lack of faith. Without the requisite spiritual fortitude, one inevitably falls prey to what Desert Father John Cassian described as "the villainies of the demons." Famously, he also coined the phrase *noonday demon*, the title of Andrew Solomon's 2011 book. It meant the monk (or whoever) had taken up at least semi-permanent residence in Satan's "foul darkness." This proto-psychological explanation of depression, with its invocations of gods and demons, proves just how much Christianity plagiarized and pillaged Greek mythology to populate its pantheon.

On the opposite side of the debate, Galen shared Hippocrates' progressive Humorist view that stress stems from imbalance among four bodily fluids: blood, yellow bile, black bile, and phlegm. Humorist theory says loss of homeostasis, loss of balance among the four humours causes disease, not demons or lack of faith.

Stress, depression, anxiety, exhaustion, burnout are nothing new. Each age, each decade, merely finds someone or something new to blame it on.

> Exhaustion has always been with us. What changes through history are the causes and effects that are aligned with exhaustion.[2]

Bottom line is that stress ain't going away soon, if ever.

Stress or distress?

If, like me, you are a stickler for precision in terminology because you understand how much words matter, you'll want to know that stress, technically speaking, is neither good nor bad. Bad stress—what we usually mean by stress—is, as a matter of fact, distress.

Not so very long ago, the words stress and distress were used almost exclusively within the engineering profession; it usually referred to inanimate materials, not living organisms.

Nowadays we tend to use distress to mean suffering, anxiety, depression—the mental anguish Buddha called dukkha. When someone says "I feel distressed," they are talking about subjective, cognitive, and emotional stress. Not the physiological response.

For our purposes, however, I use dukkha (or suffering) to describe the psychological factors that set the physiological stress response mechanism in motion.

Originally, the word stress was used by engineers to describe the change within a material when subjected to an external force. As an example, a stress test measures how much a steel beam bends when loaded down with a heavy weight. Engineers need to know how much weight a beam can support safely in order to design a building or bridge that will not fail. Today, we say "I am stressed out" when we feel overloaded with physical, mental, and emotional weight. The basic meaning is the same: we are expressing the same strained feeling, the same destructive interior state an overloaded steel beam would feel if it were human. Experts cite Walter Cannon as one of the first to use the word stress as we think of it when in 1929 he used it to describe "external factors that [disrupt] homeostasis."

After much wringing of brain cells and wrangling of terminology, I was relieved (and surprised) when I read Hans Selye's account (above). Only after "stress response" was already firmly established did he realize the confusion it was causing between the domains of physics and medicine—that he should have named it the "strain syndrome" instead. But it was too late.

While we're at it, the technical term for good stress is eustress. By the way, there are a few other medical terms in this book that are not merely confusing, not just incorrect, but downright harmful; respiratory sinus arrhythmia (RSA) is a prime example. More about that later.

The Stress Response

What do you think of when you read The Stress Response? Fight-or-flight, right? Yes, and . . . what else? What other kinds of stress responses are there?

Neither momentary nor chronic stress is inherently good or bad. Nor optional. Nor to be avoided or eliminated. What is optional is the extent, frequency, and impact of momentary and chronic stress.

That's where breath-centered practices will prove invaluable to you. When you practice one of the breath-centered techniques provided, you take advantage of breath's unique relationship with the stress response mechanism to un-trigger the stress response.

Let's begin with momentary responses. We'll examine chronic stress responses next.

Momentary Stress

Momentary stress is essential. It's the minimum degree of stress necessary for you to continue living and breathing. Without this normal, baseline stress, without the minute by minute adjustments by the autonomic nervous system—both to stay in sync with the circadian cycle and to adjust to irregular, unpredictable changes in circumstances—you'd flop to the ground and die.

STATE	DESCRIPTION
ACUTE STRESS	Severe performance breakdown; tunnel vision; catastrophic errors. Extreme incoherence.
DISTRESS	Momentary Distress: loss of stability, order, responsiveness; errors, loss of productivity. Performance declines. Incoherence.
EUSTRESS	Eustress: Peak performance. Pursuit of pleasure, thrill. The state of happiness, exuberance, joy. "The Zone." Enhanced coherence. Fun!
HOMEODYNAMIC BALANCE	Homeodynamic Balance (homeostasis): normal, health and functioning. Harmonious cooperation among all systems and processes. Integrity, Coherence.
HYPOTENSION	Insufficient response for current demands; e.g., job clock says time to work but circadian clock says time to sleep. Incoherence. Lack of energy, focus and motivation.

Momentary Stress States Continuum: Hypotension, Homeodynamic Balance, Eustress, Distress, Acute distress

Momentary Stress States

- Acute distress: severe performance breakdown; tunnel vision; catastrophic errors, extreme incoherence
- Distress: transient performance decline; loss of stability, order, responsiveness; loss of accuracy and productivity; incoherence
- Eustress: peak performance ("in the zone"); exuberance, thrill, pleasure, exhiliration; enhanced coherence
- Homeodynamic Balance: normal, healthy state of optimal functioning; harmonious 'love affair' among all systems; integrity; coherence
- Hypotension: lethargy, depression, inertia; lack of energy, focus, motivation; insufficient responsiveness for current demands; incoherence

Like death and taxes, momentary stress is one thing you can count on. Unlike those events that occur infrequently, momentary stress occurs constantly, twenty-four hours a day, day in and day out. Most of the time your body does its job so well you're not even aware of it.

Momentary stress is the cost of living—or as Buddha might say, *life is VUCA.*

Homeostasis: Essential Stress

In order to stay alive and function normally, the body continually responds to stress. All the time. Just to stay alive. Just to maintain basic functioning. Just to keep the lights on, the bills paid, and the doors open, so to speak.

This dynamic balancing act—what we know as homeostasis—requires constant data collection and analysis of many set points such as heart rate, blood pressure, hormones, brain waves, temperature. Each physiological system, cardiovascular, respiratory, digestive, endocrine, etc., monitors its own conditions second by second as circumstances change; each system modulates, tweaks its processes to maintain the conditions necessary for continued operation.

Vital Signs

Vital signs are a quick way to gauge a person's health condition. Medical professionals know these four by heart because they provide the quickest way to determine whether immediate action is required. As you might expect, the first order of business is to answer the critical question: is the patient breathing? If so, then blood pressure, pulse, and body temperature are measured. If you are not well, your vital signs will show it by falling outside these established norms:

- **Body Temperature:** 97.8 - 99.1 degrees Fahrenheit
- **Blood Pressure:** 90-120 Systolic (pressure at peak of contraction) and 60-80 Diastolic (pressure between contractions)
- **Pulse (Heart Rate):** 60-100 beats per minute while resting
- **Breath Rate:** 12 to 18 breaths per minute

Now, about breath rate. . .

Although classified as a vital sign, breathing is often not treated like one. Among all autonomic systems, breath is the forgotten child. Or, perhaps more accurately, the obvious child ignored. Especially in comparison with the cardiovascular system. Like the proverbial squeaky wheel that gets all the grease, cardiovascular problems get all the attention.

Of all the medical professionals who have taken my vitals, only one nurse actually measured my breath rate without being asked. Why is that?

Several years ago, I went to St. Agnes Hospital in Baltimore to make sure I had not broken my ankle. While I waited, one of the emergency department attendants took my vitals. In addition to the usual tests—pulse, blood pressure, weight—he also measured my breath rate. I was very surprised and curious; I could not recall having it measured before. Forever the student, I asked him, "What is normal breath rate, anyway?" To my surprise, he answered, "It depends on where you live. Different hospitals in different cities use different guidelines." I have searched several times but have not come across the guidelines he spoke of.

My theory is that we all are breathing faster than our parents, grandparents, and great-grandparents did. I also believe this trend toward faster and faster breath rates—symptomatic of hyperventilation syndrome—contributes to the epidemic of 'lifestyle diseases.' Therefore, regard any breath rate declared 'the norm' with a critical eye.

Inquiry: What is my breath rate?

Count each exhale for two minutes and then divide that number in half to arrive at an average.

Eustress: Good Momentary Stress

Homeostasis, or what I prefer to call homeodynamic balance, is wonderful—a miracle of evolution worthy of awe. It is not, however, what I mean by good stress.

It is normal to experience elevated amounts of stress in response to changing conditions. Any type of intense activity, pleasant or unpleasant, increases stress. In fact, we perform our best when our heart rate climbs above 115 beats per minute (BPM).

Distress: Productive Momentary Discomfort

Focus, coordination and overall performance are enhanced by progressively higher levels of stress. Every coach, every drill sergeant, every mentor knows, if only intuitively, that a pinch of anxiety is an essential ingredient in the recipe for excellence. Maybe that's the real reason your boss barks at you with what appears to be manufactured, made-up deadlines.

There is a fine line between eustress and distress. Focus, coordination, and overall performance are enhanced by progressively higher levels of stress, but only up to a point. As soon as you cross that line, your performance goes downhill. So where is the line? In the graph below, take note of where "Optimal arousal and optimal performance" is placed in relation to the curve's peak:

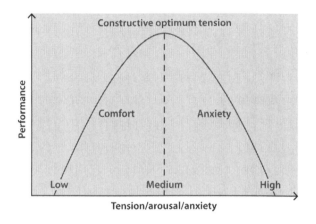

Yerkes-Dodson Law of Performance: distress
improves performance, up to a point

The 'sweet spot' falls on the right side, past the apex, on the downhill side of the curve. As long as momentary stress is what we're talking about, I have no qualms with this detail. After all, you never know what you are capable of until you push the envelope. But if this graph is intended to include chronic stress as well, then I disagree. I'll explain later when we address chronic stress.

Moderate levels of anxiety (arousal) improve performance. When incorporated mindfully into a regime, they increase resilience. Yoga, martial arts, and breath-centered practices all involve developing an acquired taste for discomfort.

I wish I had a nickel for every time I've been (playfully) accused of being a sadist. Typically, she or he glares or rolls their eyes at my instruction: Go to your edge. Push past your comfort zone. Never to the point of pain, but to that degree of sensation we in the yoga business call 'sweet discomfort.'

Do you know that to strengthen a muscle you have to weaken it, tear it down just a little? Only then does the body respond—build it up stronger.

But any level of arousal that causes the heart to beat faster than 150 or so BPM degrades performance in every way. At such extreme levels, you're no longer in the pleasure zone of eustress or the performance-enhancing zone of distress. You have crossed into the red zone; you have entered hell.

Acute Stress

The fight-or-flight response is lightning-fast. It has to be, for survival in the jungle often gets decided by which animal has the faster reaction time. In less than a second, the fight or flight response triggers mobilization of every available resource and shuts down everything not essential for the response. Heart rate (pulse) and blood pressure skyrocket so to supply the troops at the front line (cells, tissues, organs, muscles). Blood vessels turn into high-pressure fire hoses.

As soon as your heart rate exceeds 150-175 BPM (depending on your physical fitness), that sweet, peak-performance, flow-state of eustress falls apart. Whatever your personal upper limit may be, rest assured that when you exceed it your performance will deteriorate or plummet, depending on the circumstances. This breakdown can include the following sensory deficits, cognitive deficits, and motor deficits:

- Disorientation
- Tunnel vision: vision narrows to focus only on the threat, making it hard to gauge the situation in its larger context. Also, perception can be skewed by the activation of unconscious stereotypes. You do not see what's actually in front of you. In its place, you see something remembered, something you fear.
- Cognitive Tunneling, also referred to as 'survival mode,' where survival instinct eclipses perception of the current situation.
- Reliance on subconscious, 'baked-in' assumptions, stereotypes, and prejudices. Reliance on preconceived notions rather than the facts. In place of a considered or trained response, one reacts as dictated by an irrational, fear-based prediction of what the other person is going to do next.
- Neurogenic tremors, the body's natural means of discharging excess nervous energy (as in "shaking like a leaf")
- Inability to execute even the simplest tasks, to dial 911, aim accurately, or fire a weapon at all.
- If you're an athlete, you choke. If you're a public

speaker or performer, you tank from stage fright. But worst of all, as we have witnessed in the news or in person, police officers shoot when they should not, killing civilians accidentally.

Timeline of after-effects of acute stress

1. Acute Stress Reaction (ACR), commonly referred to as shock: symptoms dissipate within two days
2. Acute Stress Disorder (ASD): symptoms persist up to four weeks after the event
3. Post Traumatic Stress Disorder (PTSD): symptoms last more than four weeks after the event

It's important to understand that the threat does not have to be real. It's the thought that triggers the fight-or-flight response. This happens to all of us. It happens in mundane situations as well as in critical incidents. Thus, seeing a snake in a movie elicits the exact same reaction as encountering a real one.

When in response to a real danger—and when the body is healthy and fit enough to handle it—the fight-or-flight response can be a lifesaver. It can, literally, save your hide. But when it is not a real danger, when the threat is no more than an imagined emergency, or when the body cannot weather its extreme effects, the fight-or-flight response can be a life *taker*. Have you ever wondered why it's called a heart attack? Or why a stroke is called a stroke, as in felled by a stroke of lightning? Because it will kill you. Just ask John Henry.

The original John Henry, so the legend goes, was a hero. When the railroad company's new mechanical replacement threatened to displace him, to make him obsolete, he went head to head against the metal menace. During a public contest staged by the company, John Henry won, proving he was faster and better at driving railroad spikes. John Henry won the battle but lost the war: just moments later, the hero collapsed. The effort had sent his heart rate way over the red line. He died of cardiac arrest, paying the ultimate cost of acute stress.

Who suffers most from acute stress?

Soldiers, police officers, firefighters, and other first responders experience acute stress as a matter of course. Extreme stress responses are part of their jobs. Accordingly, these individuals receive more benefit out of breath-centered practices designed to increase resilience than anyone else.

Let's not leave out the other group exposed to acute stress and its after-effects such as trauma and PTSD. Countless men, women, and children experience acute stress through no fault of their own. These are the victims of war, street crime, car crashes, natural disaster, and so forth.

FIVE

Chronic Stress

Now, here, you see, it takes all the running you can do, to keep in the same place. If you want to get somewhere else, you must run at least twice as fast as that!

-The Red Queen (to Alice) in Lewis Carroll's Through The Looking Glass

Momentary, transient distress, what we call stress, is a natural, unavoidable part of life. Chronic stress is not. The human body is not designed to withstand stress that is persistent, prolonged, frequent—chronic.

Momentary distress turns into chronic stress when it becomes the norm and becomes your everyday normal experience. The relative ease of homeodynamic balance under conditions of normal stress gives way to dis-ease. Life becomes distressing.

THE STRESS CONTINUUM (CHRONIC STATES)	
CHRONIC ILLNESS	Hypertension. Irritable Bowel Syndrome (IBS). Diabetes. Post Traumatic Stress Syndrome (PTSD). Clinical depression.
CHRONIC DISTRESS	Dukkha. Garden variety anxiety and depression. Insomnia. Performance decline: loss of concentration and patience; mental fog and disorder; loss of productivity.
'CHRONIC' EUSTRESS	Healthy: peak creativity, productivity and performance. Unhealthy forms: addiction to extreme experiences
'CHRONIC' HOMEODYNAMIC BALANCE	Healthy, normal alternations between activity and recovery, between SNS and PSNS dominance, in accord with circadian rhythmicity. Coherence among all systems.
CHRONIC HYPOTENSION	Dull, lethargic, listless. Excessive sleep. Depression.

Chronic Stress States Continuum: chronic hypotension, 'chronic' homeodynamic balance, 'chronic' eustress, chronic stress, chronic illness (lifestyle disease)

Chronic Stress States

- Chronic Illness (lifestyle disease): hypertension; irritable bowel syndrome (IBS); diabetes; post traumatic stress syndrome (PTSD); clinical depression
- Chronic Stress: garden-variety anxiety; insomnia; persistent performance decline; loss of concentration, patience, motivation; mental fog and confusion; dukkha
- Chronic Healthy Eustress: persistent euphoria, happiness; consistent creativity and peak performance
- Chronic Unhealthy Eustress: addiction to extreme experiences such as gambling, sex, extreme sports; need to win
- 'Chronic' Homeodynamic Balance: healthy, optimal alternations between activity and rest, work and play, exertion and recovery; in compliance with natural circadian rhythms; acceptance of death as part of life cycle
- Chronic Hypotension: consistently lethargic, dull, listless; excessive sleep; chronic depression

Chronic stress is a human invention. As the author of *Why Zebras Don't Get Ulcers*[1] explains, an animal, such as a zebra, quickly recovers from acute stress. Humans get ulcers because we do not forget; acute stress lives on as somatic memory.

It's vital to remove accumulated stress. Even if you manage the balance between your capacity and your stressors well, there's a good chance your system carries the burden of accumulated stress in the form of somatic memories. Over time, this burden degrades health, vitality, and happiness. Stress could not accumulate this way if it got flushed out regularly; instead, it lodges inside your body and gums up the works.

Inquiry Question: Do you live a stress-soaked lifestyle?

Who suffers the effects of chronic stress most?

- The bereaved
- Single parents
- The poor, disadvantaged, marginalized, displaced
- Workers who are unemployed, underemployed, overworked, or who work multiple jobs

Just last night a woman who works for The Daily KOS, a progressive political advocacy organization in Washington, said,

> Whenever I'm lashing out at my coworkers like a rabid dog, I'm also not breathing! My job is so intense, so stressful that I stop breathing for who knows how long at a time.

Funny thing is, she's not even in the same building, much less the same physical office, with them. She works from the safest place in the world–her own home.

At the beginning of one workshop, I shared how my own anxiety was affecting my breathing:

> Despite the fact that I have over twenty years' teaching experience including well over 5,000 classes, right now my hands are sweaty and my breath feels tight and jagged. Now, logically, this is ridiculous. There's no reason I shouldn't be at ease. My breathing should be completely relaxed. And yet, it is not relaxed. Despite all the evidence, my reptilian brain is telling my body it's not safe to be here. That's why my breathing is tight and a little irregular.

Chronic stress—tension, anger, frustration, etc.—affects more and more of us; our daily lives are increasingly faster, more complex, more uncertain. Heart problems follow chronic stress as surely as thunder follows lightning. For this analogy to work, however, we must reverse them: chronic stress, as easy as thunder to ignore, is your early warning to avoid a future health crisis that will strike like lightning.

An epidemiologist coined the term John Henryism to describe the long-term effects of chronic stress specifically among African-American working poor in the South.[2] But John Henryism is color blind; chronic stress affects every color, race, creed, ethnicity, and socioeconomic class. The real John Henry died suddenly, struck down in his prime by a lightning bolt of acute stress. John Henryism is a long, drawn-out, slow march to the grave to the tune of a dirge.

Some degree of hypertension is a common factor in most, if not all, lifestyle diseases–regardless of race, culture, ethnicity, or geographic location. It makes no distinction between high-flying billionaires and bus-riding immigrants, between bootstrapping, hyperkinetic entrepreneurs, nor between a coal miner who lives in a small hamlet in Kentucky and a desk jockey who lives in a one-room sardine can in Tokyo. The Japanese even have a technical term for death by overwork: *karoshi*.

This job is killing me!

It's harder than ever to leave our work behind when we leave the office. At the office and at home, email and social media drain our reserves. Have you noticed how many apps, devices, appliances, and other technological products become more trouble than they're worth? In her book, *Exhaustion: A History*, Anna Katharina Schaffner writes,

In a lot of ways the technologies that were meant to save energy have become stress factors in their own right.[3]

Sound familiar?

Question: Do you push yourself to do more even when you know you may do permanent damage to your health? Are you running on sleep deficit? Will you march over the cliff with all the other lemmings? Or just expire at your desk?

The Occupational Safety and Health Administration (OSHA) has declared stress a hazard of the workplace. For example, it's estimated that task-switching, meaning switching from working on one task to a different one multiple times a day, is stressful, and results in a drastic loss of productive work being done.

Telling your boss that your poor performance is because of stress is as bad as admitting you suffer from depression. Successful people don't whine, they ignore it—or pretend to—until it's too late.

Arianna Huffington, founder of The Huffington Post, didn't see it coming. Not until she woke up in a strange bedroom one morning. Now, waking up in unfamiliar hotels was nothing new. This bedroom was indistinguishable from countless others on the dream highway. Just another overnight stay, part of the jet-set lifestyle.

But this morning was different. Huffington opened her eyes and saw blood. Her own blood. While she couldn't remember anything, it didn't take a master detective to solve the mystery. She fell asleep. Literally. Passed out from exhaustion and sleep deprivation. Took a nosedive from a full standing position. Crashed and bled.

Arianna Huffington woke up with nothing more serious than spilled blood and an ugly nose. But she also woke up to why it happened, how the race she had been running the past several years was to an early grave.

Effects of Chronic Stress on the Body

- Over stimulates the sympathetic nervous system
- Parasympathetic nervous system is under stimulated
- Disturbs balance within the enteric nervous system and results in digestive problems

Effects of Chronic Stress on the Mind

- Causes anxiety
- Causes depression
- Creates uncertainty, doubt, and results in lack of decisiveness and effectiveness

Effects of Chronic Stress on Breathing

- Causes shallow and rapid breathing pattern (hyperventilation)
- Weakens breathing, resulting in decreased gas exchange (hypoventilation)
- Causes breathing to become erratic

Compound Interest

Although less damaging than acute stress in the short term, chronic stress causes far more long-term damage because of compound interest. The problem with compound interest is that it works equally well with harmful things as with helpful things. Take hypertension as an example: by the same mathematical principle that transforms 'a penny a day' into a massive pot of gold, the cumulative effects of chronic stress accumulate until they precipitate a thunderous, unexpected heart attack.

This is what high blood pressure looks like.

Like a mole, chronic stress works underground, out of consciousness. And like the damage moles cause by burrowing tunnels beneath a beautifully manicured lawn, the damage chronic stress causes remains invisible until it's too late. It wears you down gradually, often imperceptibly, as if sneaking up behind you. Stroke, heart attack, and other forms of sudden death lie in wait, lurking behind the harmless-looking face of chronic stress. Acute stress will kill you in a flash. Chronic stress sneaks up on you; you may not even see it until it's too late.

Huffington pivoted. Ever since her awakening, her mission has been to spread the gospel of sleep. Her book, The Sleep Revolution, is a plea for sanity, for healthy work-life balance. No more nights of too little sleep. As the founder of the Huffington Post, she proselytizes the importance of rest to a global audience. She doesn't want you to make the same mistake she did. She hopes it won't take waking up in a pool of your own blood for you to wake up to the cost of burning your candle at both ends day after day.

The moral: Wake up, John Henry! Pay off your sleep debt before the interest buries you.

SIX

Disease

By 2025 stress will become the #1 public health issue–worldwide.[1]

The medical profession continues to focus on developing increasingly lethal weapons in the war on disease. Yes, the profession is slowly shifting its focus towards prevention. And this is the good news. But I want to see this shift go further and faster.

Umm, if you'll excuse me, I need a moment. I'm with my son in the emergency room – again. I'll be right back after I throttle this nurse who just asked me,

Don't you think it's just stress?

It was her tone, the way she said *"just* stress," that got me. I guess I need to explain: Before walking in tonight, my son and I discussed how we would speak, what words to say, in order to avoid a repeat of our last visit here when the hospital locked him up in the Psych Ward for two weeks.

Here we go again, I'm thinking right about now. Mind you, I do not doubt stress and anxiety are part of the story. But I also know from observing him that the answer is not black and white, not exclusively psychological nor exclusively physical. As a student of non-Western systems of health and healing, her black or white mindset is worse than non-sensical; it is harmful to my son. From where I'm sitting, the only way to solve his health problems, including the off-the-chart allergic reactions that brought us here tonight, has to account for both.

This nurse–the hospital–requires a clear-cut, black-and-white diagnosis to do anything. I understand that. What galls me is her knee-jerk conclusion; this nurse has already made up her mind. In her view, his physical symptoms are 100% psychosomatic and, therefore, not worthy of her time. Nor the hospital's.

––––––––––––––––

Anyway, what I was about to say, before getting thrown by my son's treatment, is this:

I believe that, together, we can shift the focus of medical practice away from its focus on health recovery to health creation.

In order for this paradigm shift to succeed, first, you and I have to live the change and become an inspiration to others. And in order to do that, we will benefit from learning how the medical profession came to its war footing. Fortunately, we only need to understand, in layman's terms, the difference between the fundamental assumptions of modern medicine (germ theory) and, on the other hand, the fundamental assumptions of humorism and other traditional theories.

Breath-centered practices are best thought of as proactive health cultivation rather than as treatment despite their proven efficacy as treatment. Proactive health cultivation is missing from mainstream medicine; this is why breath-centered practices are based on traditional systems like humorism, Ayurveda and traditional Chinese medicine rather than on modern medical practices.

Condition, Disorder, Syndrome, Disease

If you're like me, you're not exactly sure what causes disease, partly because you're not exactly sure what qualifies as a disease and what doesn't. Before we can even broach the question of cause, we need to agree on what a disease is—and is not.

What do you think of when you read the word disease? What comes to mind? Do you think of infection by a germ, virus, or bacteria? Like many other words, disease means different things in different contexts. The literal, original meaning is simply 'lacking ease.' Surely you agree with this simple statement: stress disturbs ease. After all, isn't that what it feels like? On the other hand, disease means something specific (and menacing) when you hear it from your doctor.

By the way, ease is more than merely the absence of disease, as you will soon see. But right now, let's see how medical experts classify symptoms of an imaginary patient lacking ease as either condition, disorder, syndrome, or disease.

Condition, Disorder, Syndrome, Disease

- **Condition:** The least specific of these four terms, condition simply means state. Being itself value-neutral, a condition can refer to either a good, healthy state or a bad, unhealthy state. In medicine, however, it usually refers to an unhealthy state. Examples of unhealthy heart conditions include angina, heart attack, heart failure, and abnormal heart rhythms, as well as many other conditions including congenital heart disease and inherited heart conditions.

- **Disorder:** A disruption to the normal or regular *functional processes* in the body or a part of the body. Heart disorders, for example, can be electrical (arrhythmia), circulatory (high blood pressure), or structural (weak or damaged heart muscles or valves). A disorder may be caused by disease, but it may also precede it and be the cause of disease. But a disorder can also exist without any disease being present.
- **Syndrome:** In medicine, a syndrome is a collection of disorders that commonly appear together.
- **Disease:** An abnormal pathophysiological change to the body's *physical structure* in response to external or internal factors which can cause both physical and emotional signs and symptoms, as well as pain, dysfunction, distress, social problems, or death. For example, diseases of the heart include cardiomyopathies (diseases that damage the heart muscles), coronary artery disease, and diseases of the heart valves.

Are you wondering why all the examples given above are heart problems while none are associated with breathing? There are a couple of reasons. The first reason is that hypertension is such a common health problem with enormous consequences. The second reason is the close connection between hypertension and hyperventilation. Simply stated, solving hypertension with breath training is the best demonstration of the power of breath-centered practices.

Disease or Malady?

Malaise and disease are so close in meaning they can be used interchangeably. And yet, I smell a rat! Slight as it may appear at first glance, I sense a clear distinction being drawn regarding culpability.

Disease (specifically as employed in modern medicine, based as it is on germ theory) implies something to the effect of, "Pathogens cause disease and, therefore, it's out of my hands. I should leave it to the professionals to cure me. It's not my fault."

Malaise, on the other hand, doesn't get a lot of airplay nowadays, having lost out to disease. To my mind, malaise belongs with humorist theory, which says the illness is caused by disruption of the homeodynamic balance between and among the organ systems of the body rather than by a germ. This is just my personal theory here, but perhaps malaise fell out of favor precisely because it implies something more like, "Had I exercised more or eaten better, just maybe my resistance would have prevented the infectious germ from ever gaining enough of a foothold to develop into a full-blown disease."

Let's examine the words disease and malaise more closely.

The -aise part of malaise comes from *aize* and means ease, exactly as in disease. The prefix *dis-* means lack of, or not. The prefix *mal-* simply means not, or "without; adding *mal-* changes the word it precedes into its opposite. In Spanish, *mal-* means bad or evil, my editor informed me the other day. To which I replied, *Yes, that's one meaning. But if you trace it back, the original meaning was a blemish, mole—essentially, a darkening of any kind.* By the way, I have read that, in Ayurvedic medicine, the word *dosha* also means blemish—a darkening of health caused by imbalance among the five elements.

Speaking of the quality 'dark,' many people believe evil is a real thing, a supernatural force or being whose one and only desire is to do you wrong. Germs, viruses and harmful bacteria are even lumped together with Satan. Disease is thought of as the embodiment of malevolence (*mal-* combined with a variant form of volition). I'm not of that persuasion. In my world, evil exists only in the eye of the labeler. Evil is simply something you don't like or want. We label anything (or anyone) we believe is harmful to our personal well-being or happiness as evil. Germs, disease, and death are evil because they go against our desire to live comfortably—forever. Conversely, we label as good anything and everything that benefits our personal health and well-being. Life is good. Living the good life is even better. Best of all, everlasting life would be simply divine, *darlin*!

Long before Buddha lived, people started searching for the root cause of disease. To arrive at its current ability to save lives and extend average lifespan by decades, the medical profession has seen innumerable theories, paradigms, tools, and clinical practices. But even today no one really knows what causes a specific person to develop a specific disease at a specific time and place. Not completely. And so the search continues.

Inquiry Question: What do you think causes disease?

Humorist Theory

The human body contains blood, phlegm, yellow bile, and black bile. These are the things that make up its constitution and cause its pains and health. Health is primarily that state in which these constituent substances are in the correct proportion to each other, both in strength and quantity, and are well mixed. Pain occurs when one of the substances presents either a deficiency or an excess, or is separated in the body and not mixed with others.[2]

Until the late 19th century, when germ theory supplanted it, humorist theory dominated medical theory and practice. None of the advanced medical technology was available back then. Neither were most of the medications we have available today. Prevention was far more important—that and natural remedies. Living according to traditional wisdom, according to time-tested principles of balance was much more important in medical practice. Living in accord with the rhythms of nature was recognized as the only way to safeguard vitality.

Ayurveda

Like Humorism, indigenous healthcare systems around the world refer to 3-5 elements that are regarded as the fundamental building blocks of the universe. In Indian Ayurveda, the sister science of Yoga, disease is said to result from imbalances between *Vata* (air and ether combined), *Pitta* (fire and water combined), and/or *Kapha* (earth and water combined). This *tri-dosha* system is a simplified, clinically-practical rendering of a five-element system—earth, water, fire, air, and *akasha* (space, or the creative impulse responsible for procreation). In the Ayurvedic theory of disease progression, a disturbance (*dushya*) within the energetic, functional systems of mind and psyche (*doshas*) will often manifest first as a mild disorder of the digestive tract. The physical ailment is a later stage of disease progression; the loss of 'homeostatic' balance precedes the ailment.

One who is established in the Self with balanced energies,

balanced digestion, well-formed tissues, proper elimination, well-functioning bodily processes, and a mind, soul, and senses full of happiness makes a healthy person.

Sushruta Samhita, verse 15.38

An Ounce Of Prevention

In the Ayurvedic concept of disease progression, doshas are the first stage, the initial symptom or condition that precedes disease. As such, correcting the imbalance is the easiest way to halt the process and avert more serious problems, including disease.

This is especially true with lifestyle diseases.

Disordered breathing, according to Yogic Ayurveda, is among the earliest symptoms indicating the progression towards disease has begun. Like other functional disorders, disordered breathing patterns manifest long before disease. Many times, I have worked with clients with what they believed were structural breathing problems only to discover there was no structural problem at all. Instead, the problem was functional. Which means the solution consisted 'merely' of retraining the breath.

Long before the disease progression shows up as structural change, it exists as functional disturbances. By the time structural changes occur, the opportunity to halt its progression has been mostly lost. At this late stage, extreme measures are typically required, measures that require surgery or drugs, or both.

Granted, there a lot in humorism that needed to be dropped, such as the belief that disease was caused by swamp gas, but there was also much in it that we need to bring back, such as an emphasis on cultivating vitality. Overly zealous doctors threw the proverbial baby out with the bathwater, so to speak. Perhaps a better way of expressing what was lost is to look at how much more profit there is in selling pills and surgery than in selling vitamins or breath-centered practices.

Germ Theory

Ever since the discovery of germs and the development of germ theory, Western medicine has focused its efforts on identifying the one pathogen, the bacteria or virus, responsible for each illness. In the process, it adopted the ideology of warfare, deploying more and more extreme weapons in the campaign to eradicate the enemy invader: chemotherapy, radiation treatment. To that end, pharmaceutical companies continue to work overtime developing 'silver bullets' that will eradicate each and every disease.

Unless and until there is a problem serious enough to require counter-attack with drugs and/or surgery, mainstream medicine has, until recently, little to offer. The nursing profession, ironically, embraces a more holistic approach and teaches nurses to honor the body's inherent healing capacity as a natural function that can be assisted but not coerced.

SEVEN

Dukkha Causes Disease

When stress is excessive, it can contribute to everything from high blood pressure, also called hypertension, to asthma to ulcers to irritable bowel syndrome. [1]

-Ernesto Schiffrin, MD, Ph.D.

My prime objective for this chapter is to convince you, dear reader, that chronic stress causes disease. Along the way, you will learn the critical role uncertainty plays in triggering the VUCA-dukkha, distress-disease progression. Armed with this knowledge, you will (I hope) be inspired to start cultivating more resilience today.

Plato famously defined health as a "consummated love affair among the organs and systems of the body." And what is the prerequisite foundation, the necessary basis for any love affair to last? Homeodynamic balance. Health is more than mere absence of disease; true health manifests as wellness, glowing vitality, ease, and episodes of happy exuberance. Sounds like romance to me!

How Chronic Uncertainty Causes Disease

Stress taxes your brain and drains your body's reserves. Every time you experience stress, regardless of whether it is pleasant or unpleasant, your brain diverts a surprisingly large percentage of the body's available energy. The brain 'steals' energy from other vital processes in order to handle the taxing situation, make sense of it, and then select your best response.

> Acute and chronic stress interferes with cognition, decision making, anxiety and mood, and in so doing affects systemic physiology through neuroendocrine, autonomic, immune and metabolic mediators and multi-morbidity of disorders frequently occurs […] In the short run, increased vigilance or anxiety in a hostile environment may be adaptive; however, when the danger passes and the behavioral state and the changes in neural circuitry become chronic, which get 'stuck', such maladaptation may require an external intervention to get it 'unstuck', as is the case for chronic anxiety or depressive disorders.[2]
>
> -Peters, McEwen, and Friston

Peters, McEwen, and Friston provide us with a new and improved definition of stress: "uncertainty about what needs to be done to safeguard physical, mental, or social well-being." The key ingredients that make a situation stressful are: no information, no control; uncertainty with a sense of threat.

Allow me to point out, in case you missed it, how eerily similar "no information, no control; uncertainty with a sense of threat" is to what we learned earlier about VUCA. Volatility means explodable or flammable. Uncertainty means you cannot determine whether it will explode in your face. Complexity means there are too many moving parts to this situation and therefore you cannot compute all the possible outcomes. Ambiguity means you aren't sure what the other person or persons involved will do next—likely because you know from experience how unpredictable people are.

To summarize: Momentary psychophysiological distress, aka the stress response, places higher demands on your system, thus increasing total allostatic load. That's all natural and normal. But when allostatic overload becomes chronic it leads to you know what—disorders, conditions, illness, and disease. In other words:

When Do I Hold My Breath? #2 (instructions)

After you have worked with simple noticing, without intervention of any kind, for at least a week, start experimenting with intervening. Choose one simple activity in which you have regularly noticed yourself holding your breath. It should be an activity where there are no time constraints or pressures, such as making your bed. Practice allowing your breath to move freely as an integral part of the activity. Notice whether or not your breathing and your movements synchronize when you breathe freely; it is not a failure if they do not!

INSPIRING ANSWERS

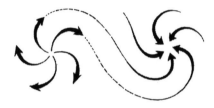

EIGHT

Introduction to Part 2

L ately, many smart, successful people in fields as diverse as health care, professional sports—and especially in resilience training programs for police officers, soldiers, and other first responders—have said the time has arrived for breath. Those of us who know the potential of breathwork have been working hard to get us to this 'tipping point' moment.

Breathwork, pranayama, breath training, and breath-centered practices go back all the way to the beginning of human culture. Conscious attention on breathing unites mind and body as nothing else can. As such, breath-centered practices are our best tool for cultivating health, well-being, vitality, productivity, and ease.

But for whatever reason, breath is not regarded by most people as important. Mainstream medicine does not encourage or support breath education or training. Most doctors, nurses, and other practitioners are simply unaware of the benefits, despite the central role breathing plays in regulating other body systems and processes.

Some say we're dreamers, some say we're visionaries. The proof, as we all know, is in the pudding.

But things are changing. More and more research is being done. In Part 2, you will discover programs that show just how effective breath-centered practices are for hypertension, anxiety, depression, asthma, body weight struggles, insomnia, post-traumatic stress disorder, and others. You are about to see why so many proclaim breath training is the next big thing.

When I started writing this book I had no intention to write about my holdup, nor about resilience training for police officers and other first responders. Freddie Grey was still alive then. For all I know, he passed me on Baltimore Street that day. There were no riots.

To persuade you to take breath-centered practices seriously, I have included the most compelling and irrefutable evidence I could find. To accomplish that, I spent countless hours finding, then studying the research. I followed the maxim every investigative reporter knows by heart, at least in the movies: follow the money trail. The research articles led me to the U.S. Military, to law enforcement organizations around the world, to firefighters, and to first responders who jump into disaster zones at the drop of a hat—or buildings toppled by earthquakes.

That's where the most persuasive evidence is. Why? It's where the funding is. Why? It's where the need is most urgent. Why? Because too many people are being shot unnecessarily due to impaired judgment caused by acute stress. Because one veteran (at least) commits suicide every 65 minutes. Because many other veterans live inside a 24/7 nightmare called PTSD. How many innocent lives could we save by providing breath-centered resilience training to every police officer, soldier, veteran, firefighter—to all first responders?

Among the millions seeking answers just like you are soldiers, police officers, firefighters, and the organizations they work for. Because lives are at stake, they need training to help them perform their jobs in critical incidents. It should come as no surprise to learn the U.S. Military is at the forefront of much of the research to develop training that increases resilience because soldiers—both active-duty and veterans—suffer the worst effects of stress, hands down. What may surprise you is the inclusion of breath-centered practices from Hindu yoga, Buddhist meditation, and Oriental martial arts. While some programs focus more on training the mind and others emphasize training the body, they all include some type of breath training. Why? Because breathing is the only autonomic function anyone can learn to observe, monitor, and control.

If you're not convinced of the power of breathwork—it's effectiveness, and therefore, it's value to you—after reading their stories, then I cannot imagine what would convince you. However, the focus of this book is on simple, easy techniques anyone can practice. Anywhere. At any time. Because we could all use more resilience. Even if it's merely rush-hour traffic we're confronting.

A Radical Notion

Shortly into my presentation the woman's hand shot into the air and waved; her face twitched as if she would burst if she didn't get a chance to speak. At first, I tried to ignore her and pretend not to be anxious speaking in front of so many strangers. Especially a couple of Hindu-looking men. Who am I to lecture to them about "Ancient Secrets of Longevity" when Hindus have practiced yoga, meditation, and breath-centered practices for millennia?

But when she continued to jerk her arm around like a fluttering flag in a hurricane, I invited her to speak. Her eyes looked as big as saucers and her voice betrayed desperate hope underneath its surface tone of incredulity as she blurted out:

One yoga instructor actually told me that if I would practice a certain way of breathing it would lower my blood pressure!

Preposterous yet far too exciting to dismiss, she seems to be saying.

Suddenly I regret all those times I've challenged the expert with a 'stump the chump' question. But this woman obviously wants it to be true. Needs it to be true, perhaps.

I notice several others' faces nodding in agreement; one elderly Hindu man actually smirks. He smiles at me as if to say, "Let's see if you know what you're talking about!" After all, it has now been 43 years since Swami Rama's famous demonstrations that, as far as I am concerned, settled this very question. Taking this interchange as an indicator of the listening I was speaking to, I decided to alter the order of my presentation. So I answered:

Excellent question! Thank you. Your teacher was right: breathing slowly and quietly—especially if you make your exhale longer than your inhale—will reduce your blood pressure. It will also slow your heart rate. And much more. The reason it works is that when you change your breathing when you make it slower, deeper, quieter and more rhythmic, the autonomic nervous system, the ANS, responds by reducing the stress response, the over-activation of the sympathetic nervous system. You may know it as the fight-or-flight response. But all you really need to know is that breathing directly affects your nervous system. When you calm your breathing, you calm your nervous system. That's what actually lowers your blood pressure. Does that answer your question?

Yes. Yes, it does. I've never heard it explained that way before.
Thank you so much!

Swami Rama Stops His Heart

Over the Easter weekend in March of 1970, Elmer Green, Alice
Green, and Dale Walters performed a number of experiments at
the Menninger Clinic with Swami Rama, a noted yogi,
specifically investigating his ability to exercise voluntary control
of bodily processes (such as heartbeat), which are normally
considered non-voluntary (autonomous). The yogi
demonstrated many abilities that impressed all those present,
including the ability to stop his heart from pumping blood for
16.2 seconds and to produce an eleven-degree difference in
temperature between different parts of the palm of his hand.
Through these experiments, Swami Rama repeatedly
demonstrated full mastery of his autonomic nervous system,
which, until then, most Western doctors had assumed was
impossible.

Years later, Swami Rama commented that the real value of his
experiments at Menninger was not to prove he could stop his
heartbeat or regulate the temperature in individual cells in his
body, but rather to demonstrate the therapeutic potential of the
mind-body connection.

NINE

Can Someone Like Me Find Peace?

*Every day I look forward to my practice, knowing
that I can use breathwork to shift into greater
joy–no matter what!*

Elena (Kim) Mawyer

I have known Elena since she started taking my class at the Yoga Center of Columbia way back in 2003, if memory serves. One day before class, not long after she became my student, Elena whispered to me, *I'm supposed to initiate you into Reiki.* I was skeptical, but intrigued.

I'll never forget the experience, although I can't describe it. The best I can do is say that I felt an electric something, like a subtle bolt of lightning traveled from her hands into my whole being. It lasted a second or less, and yet there was something different from that moment on. Needless to say, I was no longer skeptical about Reiki.

Elena and I have been friends now for over fifteen years. She married a Spaniard, and lives in Madrid. More than anyone else, Elena has helped bring this book to fruition. She may not be a professional editor, but her contributions have been invaluable. We've known each other for so long, and we trust each other so much, that Elena knows she can call me out (and vice versa).

For example, during one Skype meeting, Elena stopped, stared at me for a second, and then asked: *Are you sleeping? I've never seen you this stressed out before. Please don't be offended, but I have to ask you: Are you practicing what you preach? Are you doing any of the breath-centered practices in this book? When's the last time you meditated?*

In addition to serving as a trusted sounding board and critic, Elena has actually incorporated breath-centered practices into her daily life. Let's hear what Elena has to say:

> I have fibromyalgia, which for me means migraines, anxiety, joint pain, insomnia, irritable bowel syndrome, dizziness, and fatigue, among other symptoms. Sometimes it feels like my body is seeking out new and creative ways to torment me. I've been a yoga and meditation practitioner for nearly 20 years, though lately my practice is limited and sporadic. However, I have been practicing breathwork for over 400 days straight, without missing a single day. So I pose this question to you: is it possible to access states of bliss while your physical reality is chronic illness? How can a person like me find peace in the midst of daily suffering?
>
> For me, breathwork has been different from other practices. It doesn't feel like just another item on my to-do list, like something I "should" do. It's truly a pleasure, a kind of oasis in my day. I may be suffering for 23 and a half hours a day, but during my breathwork practice, I can usually find peace.
>
> For some of my symptoms, breathwork actually helps to

alleviate them. For instance, since the digestive system is right next to the respiratory apparatus, they affect each other in a very direct way. I know that when I'm experiencing nausea or stomach pain, my first impulse is to hold my breath. I don't want to feel what's going on in my body. Yet this contraction ultimately creates more digestive distress, feeding a vicious cycle. I'm often able to identify and release tension I didn't realize I was carrying via breathwork. Indeed these practices are often the solution to help ease some of my discomfort. But sometimes, it's more about changing my perspective on what I'm feeling. It's about moving into the position of an observer, watching the tornado all around me without being drawn into it. To be honest, some days I don't achieve that. Other days I do.

The first time I tried Coherent Breathing™, using the recording Coherent Breathing Symphony, I remember telling Joe it was as effective as a sedative. In fact, I played the recording over again because I wanted more. I believe even just trying these practices once will convince you like it convinced me, and you won't want to stop either. Nowadays my daily breathwork practice usually entails some combination of Coherent Breathing™, Diaphragmatic Breath, and Sitali Breath. I have done breathwork in international airports, on the metro, in a car while carsick, in a doctor's waiting room, and in a dentist's chair while having cavities filled. I'm trying to find the balance between a dedicated daily practice and also remembering to integrate breathwork into my life. Whenever I find myself wanting to skip my practice, which is not very often, it's usually because I'm hiding from something on a psychological level. These practices can be challenging. They can bring up difficult experiences, tears, anxiety, memories, and revelations. Sometimes it's painful, but in the end, I feel better having peeled back a few layers. Breathwork helps me let go, to move out of distress and into health, seeking bliss. It's a work in progress, but I have important tools now for whatever I face in a day.

My Ayurvedic doctor once said to me, "This [suffering] is not your true nature. Your true nature is bliss." We are disconnected from the bliss of our true nature, from the pleasure of breathing. In breathwork, I have found a way to alleviate some of my symptoms, yes, but more importantly, to achieve peace by changing my relationship with my illness. Every day I look forward to my practice, knowing that I can use breathwork to shift into greater joy—no matter what!"

TEN

Curing Hypertension

Within the past five years, scientific research has clearly demonstrated the effectiveness—and cost-effectiveness—of certain stress-reduction therapies in the prevention and treatment of disease. For example, heart disease, America's No. 1 killer, and its primary risk factor, hypertension, can be largely prevented—and even reversed—through simple, scientifically proven methods of stress reduction and lifestyle modification.[1]

I have painted a grim picture of the ravages of stress, but now it's time to flip the coin and see stress as an opportunity. Breath-centered practices restore balance and thereby cause ease. Ease is not mere relaxation, ease is the state of wholeness, integrity, and coherence. Ease is optimal functioning. This is how breath-centered practices restore health and vitality to the whole person. When you learn to do that you will be able to avoid the harmful effects of chronic stress and the lifestyle diseases that result. Sounds great, doesn't it?

One of the many effects of chronic stress is disordered breathing. Conversely, disordered breathing can cause stress, anxiety, and many other problems. A prime example of this reciprocal cause-and-effect link is the connection between hyperventilation and hypertension. The respiratory system is unique because it, unlike all the other autonomic systems, affords both automatic and manual control. Only breathing can readily be made conscious and voluntary. This is the anatomical basis of all breathwork.

Just yesterday I was talking to a friend of a friend who happens to be a retired internist. When we got into talking about my book, about this chapter on the relationship between hypertension and hyperventilation, his expression turned . . . into what I couldn't tell. So I asked him,

> *You haven't heard of the connection? Or do you disagree that there is one?*

> *I've never heard it before,* he replied.

If you're reading this, Tom, here's what I would have said, had my mind not been on other things:

The Hyperventilation Connection

The role of anxiety and tension in hypertension has long been a subject of debate [...] Papers in the medical and psychiatric literature state that hyperventilation causes vasoconstriction and increases of blood pressure, even though a classic early study of the hemodynamic effects of voluntary hyperventilation concluded that hyperventilating for one minute lowered [blood pressure]. So, who is right? The answer is possibly both. [...] hyperventilation itself does lower blood pressure, and it is only when panic is superimposed that the pressure goes up.

Thomas Pickering, M.D., D.Phil.

A Bridge Too Far?

Given that the typical adult (at sea level) breathes between 10 and 20 times per minute, does suboptimal breathing not play a significant part in the present hypertension pandemic? Of course it does!

Stephen Elliott, The New Science of Breath, pg. 18

Our modern medical system does not recognize the importance of breathing habits as the central regulator of the body's systems. Breathing is so simple, and so seemingly inconsequential that to even entertain the possibility that merely breathing slower and deeper lowers blood pressure beggars belief. Consequently, there is little or no interest on the part of doctors and others in the healthcare mainstream to encourage or support breath education or training. When he tries to advocate for breath awareness and breath-centered practices as a valuable tool for cultivation of health and wellness, Dr. Weil says his words are met with, at best, a lack of interest. Oftentimes, the notion is met with derision or scorn.

In most people in our culture, the tone of the sympathetic system is much too high. There are all sorts of reasons for that . . . all the stimulation in the environment, stress. . . But most of us go through life with things tilted in that direction, and that is responsible for all sorts of problems like high blood pressure, circulatory problems, digestive problems, and so forth. Of all the methods I've seen for relaxation, the most time effective and cost effective are breathing techniques.

[...]

[Breath work is] . . . not even on the radar screen of conventional medicine. It's not taken seriously because it's too simple. It makes use of something right under your nose, it requires no equipment, its free. If just this one thing was brought into mainstream medicine . . . cut costs, cut adverse outcomes, improve medical effectiveness.

Andrew Weil

And so to propose breath-centered practices as a solution for the global hypertension epidemic may sound ludicrous. A bridge too far. But that is precisely what I am claiming: **there is a free alternative treatment for hypertension!**

Furthermore, I believe every child should be taught Coherent Breathing™ and/or Diaphragmatic Breathing as a way to modulate her or his blood pressure.

In *Breathe Well, Be Well*, Dr. Robert Fried provides a dramatic example of the benefits of Diaphragmatic Breathing for hypertension:

Victor is a thirty-two-year-old professional. He is married and has no children. Well above average in height and of athletic build, he came to see me because of borderline hypertension. In addition, he reported mild tension associated with his work schedule but otherwise appeared to be in good health. His breathing rate was found to be 18 b/min with CO_2 (3.92%) well below the normal limit for his body build. This is a hyperventilation pattern. It came as a surprise to him that he was breathing predominantly with his chest–he's just never thought about it. His BP was initially 150/89.

Within a matter of minutes, his new patient lowered his own blood pressure with nothing more than deep, slow, diaphragmatic breathing:

> . . . his breathing rate dropped to 4.75b/min with normalized CO_2 (4.88%). At that point, his BP was 137/89. After four once-per-week training sessions, his breathing dropped further to 3b/min during training, with normal CO_2 (4.98%), and his BP went from 133/75 before the breathing exercise to 126/72 after it. After the fourth session, there was no further need to see me and he terminated treatment.

Armed with the ability to control his own blood pressure, Victor left with a new breathing habit, not a prescription drug habit. Shouldn't everyone be taught Diaphragmatic Breathing in school as part of physical education? How much pain, suffering—and money—would that save?

How many breaths do I breathe per minute? (instructions)

1. Count your exhales over the course of two minutes using some kind of external timer you can set, that will alert you when two minutes have passed.
2. Do not watch the clock as you count. It's hard enough to breathe normally doing any breath inquiry. Watching the second hand will definitely change your breathing and skew the results!
3. Afterward, divide the total in half to arrive at your breath rate (BR).

ELEVEN

Inspired By Example

Practicing regular, mindful breathing can be
calming and energizing and can even help
with stress-related health problems ranging
from panic attacks to digestive disorders. Since
breathing is something we can control and
regulate, it is a useful tool for achieving a
relaxed and clear state of mind. Breath is the
key to health and wellness, a function we can
learn to regulate and develop in order to
improve our physical, mental and spiritual
well-being.[1]

Andrew Weil

I want to impress upon you the primacy of experience over 'book learning.' Take Jodi, for example. For her final project in yoga teacher training, she wrote an impressive paper documenting research findings that validate the effectiveness of breathwork and yoga for treating asthma. But more importantly, she shared her personal experience of curing her own asthma!

Jodi's Asthma

Several years after developing asthma I was looking for a yoga class. I had wanted to start practicing yoga and had tried a number of different beginner-level classes off and on for a couple of years. But I never found one that I really liked.

Then I took Joe Roberson's Saturday morning Level-1 Yoga class at the Yoga Center of Columbia. I loved this class and I loved yoga, the way that I thought I would if I could find the right class and the right instructor. I started taking weekly yoga classes with Joe and I have continued to do so now for many years. The classes included Hatha yoga and Kundalini yoga.

After one or two years of practicing yoga regularly, I noticed that my asthma had improved substantially. I was really surprised because it never crossed my mind that doing yoga could have a positive impact on my asthma. Looking back, I believe that it was the kapalabhati in Kundalini yoga, in particular, that had the greatest impact. However, I think that I can credit all pranayama for my better health.

When I noticed that my asthma symptoms had improved, I decided to stop taking my medications and see what would happen. It turned out that I didn't need them and I haven't used them since then. It's been a few years and my doctor is impressed that my asthma symptoms are still under control with yoga and only my albuterol inhaler.

Brenda's Weight

At the beginning of class, week seven of a 12-week course I was teaching, I asked who would be willing to share what she or he had gained so far. Brenda wowed us all by saying, "I have dropped 34 pounds since the first week of class." The expressions on other students' faces were a mix of admiration and skepticism, as you might imagine. Even I doubted her claim. I'd never heard of such a thing before! One woman across the room asked, "You mean, along with a strict diet, right?"

To which Brenda replied,

> *Nope. Just from what I've learned from observing my breath. While eating dinner after that first class, I noticed something. It was a few minutes into our meal. I was half, maybe two-thirds, into what I usually eat. I knew I'd never heard it before. Guess I'd always been too busy enjoying my food to hear it. It was a subtle sound like . . . I dunno, like a sigh. This sound, I realized, was my body's way of saying "enough." I instinctively knew I had heard, for the very first time, the sound of satiation, my body's spontaneous expression for, "Enough food, you should stop now."*
>
> *Since then I have honored that signal by putting down my knife and fork and pushing the plate away. I've started spending the time not eating being with my husband. So, my home practice for the past six weeks consists of listening for that breath, that sound. When I do, I stop eating. That's it.*

Inquiry Question: "When Do I Hold My Breath?" #3

Inquiry: Is my stomach interfering with taking a deep breath because I ate so much? How are different mental and emotional states reflected in my breathing pattern? Do I honor my body's hunger signal or do I ignore it and keep eating for emotional reasons?

Set aside one meal a day in which you do not feel any time constraints. Let yourself breathe slowly as you eat. Notice how it feels to allow your belly to release as you chew and swallow your food. Observe whether or not your meal is more enjoyable. If you tend to overeat or have digestive problems, did monitoring your breathing help you stop eating when you felt your stomach becoming full? How did you feel during and after the meal?

Ed's Insomnia

An avid scuba diver and sailor, Ed asked me one day after class if I might be able to help him with some breathing problems. He wanted to try something, anything that might help him avoid surgery. His doctor recently recommended a procedure that would remove portions of the sinus bones impeding airflow to improve Ed's breathing and, in consequence, his insomnia. My gut feeling was that Ed had a functional problem, not a structural one.

We ended up meeting for four private sessions. In our first meeting, Ed explained that he couldn't remember when the habit of breathing through his mouth began. It was such an ingrained habit he didn't even realize he could breathe through his nose. When scuba diving, one has to breathe through the mouth; thus, it strengthened Ed's preexisting habit, his functional pattern of mouth breathing.

Long story short, Ed never had surgery and sleeps much better since he learned to breathe better. What Ed's doctor diagnosed as a structural problem that only surgery could correct, turned out to be 'merely' a functional problem. A matter of habit, not of physical deformity or disease. The only remedy that made sense was breath pattern retraining. That's what Ed proceeded to do, with a bit of guidance from me.

Recently, I asked Ed if he would be willing to share his side of the story by sending me an account to be included here. In that initial request, I asked three questions:

1. Why did you want to learn to breathe better?
2. What did you learn?
3. What benefits have you experienced from changing how you breathe?

ED'S RESPONSE:

> I went to Yoga Joe because I was experiencing shortness of breath and I have sleep apnea. I have used a CPAP whenever I sleep, even to take a short nap, for several years.
>
> Joe taught me breathing exercises and chest-opening yoga poses. The breathing exercises and yoga poses increased my lung capacity and I was able to take deeper breaths. I slept better because I was able to breathe easier. Sleeping better resulted in overall better health. The positive results were almost immediate and I still practice what Joe taught me to maintain my good health.

A DAY OR TWO LATER I RECEIVED THIS ADDITION:

> Thanks for all of your help. I didn't realize until I checked how much of a positive impact that you had on my health.
>
> After thinking about this for a while I decided to look at my Fitbit data to see if there was documentation of your treatment. There was a dramatic change in my sleep from about five hours of sleep per night to an average of over eight

hours of sleep per night. Prior to treatment, I was awake or restless for almost one hour for every hour I slept. After treatment, I am awake or restless for only one hour per night and I am sleeping for about eight hours for every hour awake or restless, according to my Fitbit dashboard.

I WROTE BACK:

Ed,

This is great. But a piece is missing. If I remember correctly, you avoided surgery by learning to breathe differently. Correct?

TO WHICH ED REPLIED:

Actually, you are correct. I had blotted that memory from my consciousness. I was incorrectly diagnosed with emphysema. I left it out because the diagnosis was incorrect and I thought that would just confuse my story. The story is an MRI showed a small mark on one lung. A technician flagged it. A specialist later looked at several MRIs several years apart and saw the same spot had not changed so he concluded that it was nothing.

[…]

I was having my teeth straightened by a dentist using Invisalign. The dentist thought that my sleep apnea was related to the structure of my jaw. I went to the University of Maryland Dental School where they recommended a three-part plan. The plan would require me to wear braces for about six months, then have surgery to remove mandibular tori[2] from my lower jaw. Then have another surgery to move my jaw forward. And finally, I would need to wear braces again to make any adjustments needed to correct my bite. Because I am now able to sleep for eight hours a night I no longer feel the need to take additional measures to treat my sleep apnea. More than one orthodontist, several dentists, and a pulmonologist strongly discouraged me from moving forward with the surgery that was recommended because it would be extremely painful and may not correct my sleep apnea.

I am currently sleeping well using a CPAP and doing yoga and breathing exercises.

Hikers on the Appalachian Trail

I've had nearly-identical conversations with numerous thru-hikers on the Appalachian Trail, those extraordinary individuals who hike the entire 2,181 miles from Springer Mountain in Georgia to Mount Katahdin in Maine. I've never done it myself; I just camp out at Bears Den, a lodge next to the AT in Virginia, when I need its mountain setting and fresh air to rejuvenate my writing.

Each conversation starts out something like this:

What's your book about?

It's about breathwork. You know, as in yoga, breath, meditation.

Oh. I can't meditate. I tried, but I can't sit still long enough. Besides, I can't stop my brain. It races all the time, even when I'm trying to go to sleep. I can't make it stop.

I say I understand. Then I seize the opening and say:

Can I ask you something? Have you ever found yourself just walking? What I mean is, haven't you the experience where the only thing you're doing is walking? You're not thinking about the past. You're not thinking about the future. When you're doing what you're doing while you're doing it—and nothing else?

Um, well, sure. I guess. But that's not meditation. It sometimes happens when I stop to admire the view. The sunrise. Or a rainbow. A flower by the trail.

That's meditation! Maybe you've heard called the flow state. You're simply doing what you're doing while you're doing it.

At this point, their face transforms from embarrassment to puzzlement, and finally to recognition. A light switches on and their face brightens:

You mean that's all there is to it?

Yes! Meditation is just a technique that helps you experience flow without beautiful scenery or a flower or a rainbow. You don't need big, fancy words. You don't need a complicated technique or a secret mantra. And you most definitely don't have to be able to stop your mind from thinking!

Would you like to hear a simple and easy technique you can do while you're hiking?

Yes!

Okay. All you need to do is to count your steps and sync them with your inhales and exhales. Like this:

Wow! Thanks for the tip! I'm going to try it tomorrow on the trail.

Ready to take the miracle cure? Feel free to jump straight to *Walking Coherence* in Part 5, Instructions.

TWELVE

Death by Unreasonable Panic

I t started as a routine traffic stop.

Officer Jeronimo Yanez pulled Diamond Reynolds over for a broken taillight. Moments later, 32-year-old Philandro Castile, nutrition services supervisor at J. J. Hill Montessori Magnet School, was dead. Why? Reynolds says Philando Castile was just doing what Yanez ordered him to do–reaching for his ID. Yanez, on the other hand, says Castile was reaching for his gun. Yanez pulled the trigger seven times, out of mortal fear.

As her four-year-old daughter watches from the back seat, Ms. Reynolds calmly live-streams the next 10 minutes to Facebook. The video shows Castile's blood-drenched body, head lolling slightly. We hear him mumble. We see his eyes shift, then close. We hear Ms. Reynold say,

Oh God, don't tell me he's dead! Please don't tell me my boyfriend just went like that. . . please don't tell me that he's gone.

Through the passenger window, we see the officer's weapon poised to put another bullet into Philando Castile's dead body. We hear the officer's erratic breathing as he gasps, then screams

> *Keep your hands where they are! Fuck! Huuawh! I told him not to reach for it! I told him to keep his hands off it!*

Diamond Reynold's live-streamed Facebook video went viral. She became the spokesperson for the nationwide struggle for all who believe "The police are not there to protect and serve us, they are there to assassinate us." Long weeks of protests ensued, some violent themselves, against police brutality, racism, and unwarranted shootings of civilians. Officer Yanez was charged with three felonies: one count of second-degree manslaughter and two counts of dangerous discharge of a firearm. Reynold's video was admitted as court evidence.

> We pull people out of wrecked cars, we hold people's hands when they're dying, we talk to 5-year-olds when they get raped, and one cop puts a chokehold on somebody and all of a sudden we're all racist killers.[1]

A Case Of Unreasonable Panic

During trial, John Choi, attorney for Ramsey County, condemned Officer Yanez's performance during those fateful few seconds that stole Philando Castile's breath forever. Choi told the judge and jury,

> *...no reasonable officer knowing, seeing, and hearing what Officer Yanez did at the time would have used deadly force under these circumstances.*[2]

Reynold's amateur documentary film, shot with only her

smartphone, delivered instantly and globally, thanks to Facebook, now and forevermore is safely archived inside that virtual safe deposit box we know as the internet.

Reflecting back on the trial, Choi addressed the elephant in the room–the burning question about the role unconscious, implicit racism played in Yanez' decision to pull the trigger:

> …we have to recognize that …we all come to our life or our situations with our own life experiences. We all have biases based upon how we were raised and our professional experiences inform our judgments and our decisions. Everybody in this world has it. It's actually a survival mechanism, so in that context, was there implicit bias in this case? Well, I think in every context of police interaction there is that implicit bias. I have an implicit bias as I sit here today based on my life experiences. Now if we are talking about (whether) Officer Yanez intentionally shoot Philando Castile because of his race, the answer would be no, I don't think so. The real problem? Lack of effective training. We fail our police by not providing resilience training that could prepare them to make clear-headed decisions in critical moments like Officer Yanez faced.[3]

Acute Stress Impairs Police Officers' Performance

How can we expect an officer to make a clear-headed decision in circumstances where you or I would either faint or act like a wild savage? Racial bias is clearly part of the problem. But I don't believe for a minute that officers are out to assassinate black men—or anyone. As Bill Johnson, executive director of the National Association of Police Organizations, a coalition of police units and associations from across the United States, explains:

Most officers are devastated when they kill someone on the job, even if they're convinced they had no other choice. [...] Some would be silent, some guys would cry, some would be sick. . . . But no one was ever happy. About half the officers eventually leave their jobs.[4]

Across the country, police departments are looking for ways to answer the public's demands to end racism and brutality. What was an already challenging profession has become a pressure cooker. Demoralized, officers are afraid to do their jobs. They know they have become targets. On January 20, 2017, Officer Michael Louviere responded to a crash scene in Jefferson Parish, Louisiana. As he kneeled over Simone Veal, who had multiple gunshot wounds, Officer Louviere was shot in the back of the head. Both died.

Stress is an unavoidable, essential factor of living. Only when it increases enough to become noticeable do we say we feel stressed. Fact is, at moderate levels—when heart rate is between 115 and 145 beats per minute (BPM)—stress enhances performance. But when heart rate exceeds 150 BPM performance starts to fall apart: motor skills—the dexterity to aim and shoot a weapon or dial a phone number—disintegrate. And at a heart rate faster than 170 BPM, you become, effectively, blind, deaf, and dumb.

I was in a gunfight in a hallway [...] You have never experienced the kind of stress you feel when you're in a real fight when somebody's trying to kill you. You're going to lose your peripheral vision. You won't hear your partner yelling things. The higher your heart rate, the more you get cognitive deterioration.[5]

-Dave Glennon

I experienced this myself when I was robbed by a gang of black teenagers. Two handguns, one by either cheek, put the fear of God in me. Fortunately, I have resilience from practicing yoga, breathwork, and meditation. I'm convinced my ability to remain relatively calm saved my life that day.

In critical moments, such as the one faced by Officer Yanez, an officer must be able to think straight. They need resilience. Luckily, resilience is not fixed at birth, like a personality trait. It can be developed and strengthened. Resilience training prepares first responders for the internal 'fog and friction' acute stress causes.

Resilience training

What is resilience? In the context of police, military, fire, and other first responders, resilience is one's capacity to "face the most extreme circumstances (and be able to continue) doing your job on any given day" (Lieutenant-General Jonathan Vance, Chief of Defence Staff of the Canadian Armed Forces. 2015).

Resilience training builds the capacity to perform—to make rational decisions and do your job as trained—in critical moments of acute stress.

It should come as no surprise to learn that the search for a solution is being led by the military. What may surprise you is the inclusion of mind-breath-body practices from Hindu yoga, Buddhist meditation, and Oriental martial arts in many of the studies. While some programs focus more on training the mind while others emphasize training the body, they all include some type of breath training. Why? Because breathing is the only autonomic function anyone can learn to observe, monitor and control.

To me, the most promising programs are the ones that combine ancient breath-centered practices with hi-tech biofeedback. The iPREP program, for example, includes *instruction and use of biofeedback to practice engaging in controlled breathing ... [which research has shown can] enhance SNS [sympathetic nervous system] control during stress.*[6] Wearable biofeedback systems, such as the Smart Shirt developed at Georgia Tech, make it possible to analyze the stress response of an individual, identify that person's triggers, and then customize the training to make it even more effective. Beyond the initial resilience training, this system can function as a hi-tech job-performance aid, both while the officer is on duty and off. It's meant to accompany her or him from the first day in the force through the last.

The benefits of resilience training are many and are not limited to performance during a high stakes critical incident. Another big benefit is better overall health. Any increase in resilience decreases chronic stress, a huge problem for first responders in general. For example, active-duty police officers who participated in one mindfulness-based study reported improved sleep quality. Other benefits documented include reduced PTSD-related symptoms, less fatigue, less hyperarousal, anxiety, and depression. Additionally, it's not unreasonable to assume some would experience relief from suicidal thoughts and urges —and actual suicides.

Police Officers Make Better 'Shoot/Don't Shoot' Decisions After Resilience Training

What evidence exists that this training actually improves decision-making during confrontations? After one police training, participants *displayed significantly enhanced situational awareness, overall performance, and made a greater number of correct use-of-force decisions (shoot/no shoot) than officers in the control group. ... Improved performance directly translates into potential lifesaving decisions for police and the civilians they are working with.*[7]

Let's make this happen.

We have solid evidence that resilience training works, that it has the potential to make America's streets safer. I firmly believe it will save black lives, white lives, red lives, yellow lives—all colors. It can save officers' lives, too. We have to make resilience training standard in every police department, large and small, so that what starts out as a routine traffic stop—like the one that ended Philando Castile's life and Officer Yanez' career—has a better chance of ending as one. As Lindsay Wise and Katy Moeller explain, *It's going to take both sides. . . . If we squander the opportunity, then we'll just continue to muddle along the way we have, which would be a tragedy on top of tragedy.*[8]

THIRTEEN

Chronic Emotional Distress

---

*The breath is a key to your emotional state because
it both reflects and affects your level of tension.
Learning to breathe with full feeling gives you
the ability to inspire yourself.*[1]

O kay, folks. This is where it gets real.

The singer, Chris Cornell, founding member of
Soundgarden and Audioslave, hanged himself.
While I've never been an ardent fan, the song "Fell on Black
Days" has played non-stop like an anthem during my own
black spells. Loud.

Chris Cornell was famous. He was handsome, incredibly
talented, and very successful. That's why his suicide shocked so
many people. He hanged himself in his hotel room two hours
after giving a wonderful concert. It makes no sense why he
would want to end it at all, much less at that moment. Then
again, mental illness, by definition, makes no sense.

You cannot convey the reality of depression to someone who

has not felt it. It's not possible. How can you describe how the world changes, utterly, when the darkness descends? One day, your world is lit with possibility and then the next day, it's all black. It's as if the movie projector bulb burned out. Depression cannot be described, much less solved, as though it is just an error of thinking. It changes you at a much deeper level than mere thinking. It alters your perceptions, the colors you see and the smells you smell.

When someone famous like Chris Cornell or Robin Williams takes their own life it's news. But for every famous person, many others we never hear about also reach the same conclusion, that taking one more breath would simply be one too many. I have lost friends and acquaintances. Have you?

On the other hand, there is one group we have been hearing about lately: veterans. When I was growing up, it was veterans returning from Vietnam with drug addiction or a sexually transmitted disease, an STD. Today, our veterans are returning home from Iraq and Afghanistan with PTSD. And they are committing suicide. Those who don't go on tolerating their suffering each day.

P.S., My brother, Mike Roberson, took his own life on February 6, 2018.

––––––––––

There is now sufficient data to conclude that immune modulation by psychosocial stressors or interventions can lead to actual health changes, with the strongest direct evidence to date in infectious disease and wound healing. Furthermore, recent medical literature has highlighted a spectrum of diseases whose onset and the course may be influenced by pro-inflammatory cytokines, from cardiovascular disease to frailty and functional decline; pro-inflammatory cytokine production can be directly stimulated by negative emotions and stressful experiences and indirectly stimulated by chronic or recurring infections. Accordingly, distress-related immune dysregulation may be one core mechanism behind a diverse set of health risks associated with negative emotions.

How Depression Affects Breathing

I guess I'm what you might call a 'walking depressive,' the same way an alcoholic who is able to function more or less normally is called a walking alcoholic. I function quite well despite my depression—mostly. Most of the time. Because I'm a yoga teacher, I've avoided talking about my depression. I mean, who wants to take a class with a depressed teacher who'll infect them with their funk? People seek out a teacher whose presence is inspiring so they can be lifted up. So, I've kept it private as much as possible.

Which comes first, depressed mood or listless diaphragm? The other night, I shared with my students how depression literally depresses the movements of the diaphragm. I have observed, in my own experience, how little my diaphragm moves when I'm feeling listless and unmotivated. What's worse is that I also lack the willpower to make it move more, to take even one deep diaphragmatic breath. As I told the group, when I'm laid out in bed, unable to move, it's like my diaphragm is listless and unmotivated, too.

Washing Depression Down The Shenandoah River

Journal entry from 2011:

"Wanna go for a walk?"

"Sure. I guess. Not getting anything done here. Might as well."

We drove from Baltimore out to the Press Corps Monument Park near Harpers Ferry. The Appalachian Trail passes right through the park.

My feet are making this annoying sound as they scrape the ground. "Joe, lift your goddamn feet!" I admonish myself. But I'm so depressed, I don't want to lift my ribs—much less my feet.

An hour or two later, we're wading out into the Shenandoah River. The water is cool and green, the rocks are slippery. At some point, I dunno why, I start dunking my head under. Just to feel something.

I hold onto the edge of an underwater rock so I don't get carried downstream so I can try practicing Sudarshan Chakra Kriya. To see if I can get out from under this black cloud. I inhale as big and deep a breath as I can. Then I hold my breath underwater while I pumping my navel 16 times–repeating "Wahe Guru!" with each pump.

Again. Again. And again.

After who knows how many times of this, I stand up. The Shenadoah and Harpers Ferry and the sky and everything looks and feels real now. Feels solid. I feel solid again. My eyes can see what's in front of me.

Hallelujah, I'm breathing again!

Time spent practicing breathwork is time spent attending to the heart of things, to what really matters. When you practice breathwork, you collect and integrate all your parts—physical, mental, emotional, spiritual. This, in turn, will give you a little more freedom to be you, all of you, good, bad, indifferent. When you are authentically present, it's much easier to pursue —and enjoy—happiness on your own terms. Released from fear, you are free! Free to accept what is or to take action to change it. Free to choose how to respond instead of reacting out of habit.

When Do I Hold My Breath? #4 (instructions)

Begin to monitor your breathing during telephone conversations, noticing whether you allow yourself to pause when you need time to think, whether you allow the other person to complete his/her sentences before interrupting and whether you feel your breathing supporting your voice. Can you tell whether the person on the other end of the line is holding their breath? Can you identify their pattern? Gradually start to integrate this into more casual conversations.

Your graduation exam for this exercise is to practice breathing during an argument or confrontation. How does this practice change the way you interact with others and the outcome of your interactions?

FOURTEEN

Veterans with PTSD

I found myself weeping when Dr. Brown said, "Think of those you love." I came away with a sense of being reunited with my life and loved ones. For the first time in years, I wanted to be connected to something besides a war or a disaster zone. After the breathing, during the meditation, I felt connected to the universe and to everyone in it.[1]

Breathwork is powerful medicine. Its effectiveness as a natural therapeutic modality has been esteemed since ancient times. Some of these are beyond the scope of this book, which for the most part, is limited to easy, simple, and harmless practices anyone can incorporate into their daily life. But the breathwork techniques, practices, and protocols under discussion here require expert instruction, support, and guidance, at least initially. Some are not for the faint of heart. But the rewards are worth it, in terms of resolving emotional blocks, opening to expanded awareness and states of consciousness. When warranted, these are exactly what the doctor ordered! I like to call them "industrial strength cleaners." And what I find especially encouraging is that some of these less-known practices are emerging from the fringe and showing up in the most surprising places.

The Breath Cure

You won't find a more heartwarming example of breathwork's potential than this one. The early results are in, and they indicate this breathwork-based protocol works at least as well as conventional treatments with antidepressant medications and psychotherapy. And it costs far less. Veterans suffering from PTSD are being helped—maybe even cured—by breathwork.

Power Breath Meditation (PBM) is based on Sudarshan Kriya, the flagship practice taught by Ravi Shankar's Art of Living Foundation. Sudarshan Kriya is nowhere near as wild and crazy as some I have tried. On the other hand, you won't encounter it in your typical yoga class. Like Yoga Nidra (rebranded as iREST for the military), Sudarshan Kriya has been modified, customized, and rebranded to gain acceptance into military culture.

A longitudinal study in 2013 found strong evidence that Power Breath Meditation really does work, evidence that it reduces symptoms of PTSD. Compared against the control group, the veterans who participated in the seven-day workshop exhibited *reduced PTSD symptoms, anxiety, and respiration rate. [...] These findings are promising given that of the three PTSD symptoms, hyperarousal yields the strongest influence on health-related quality of life in returning veterans [... the] benefits . . . endured independently of continued practice.*[2]

Let me hammer home that last bit: When these vets were re-evaluated one year later their symptoms were unchanged—

whether or not they continued practicing! The effects did not fade or disappear, as might be expected. Was their PTSD cured permanently? If so, how? What is it about PBM that accounts for its effectiveness? As Leslye Moore, National Director of the program, told me,

> [Power Breath Meditation] actually gets at the root of PTSD.[3]

First of all, PBM works because it provides a safe space, a safe time, and clear and supportive guidance on precisely how to relive the event such that it is fully experienced. Once fully experienced, the memory naturally fades because it has finally been—once and for all time—properly processed. The experience that caused PTSD was so horrific the person literally bales, disassociates, because that's the only way to live through it. The original traumatic experience has never been experienced, not fully lived. Like a tormented soul who can neither exit the worldly plane nor enter the next, a person with PTSD is a ghost, a disassociated psyche. And the only solution is to return to the scene of the trauma and experience it without dissociating. In short, you gotta go through it to get past it. There is no other way, no substitute. More conventional treatments miss the mark; to be specific, they merely cover up, camouflage, distract, numb.

FIFTEEN

ACE of Hearts

---

*Four sessions of breathwork did more for me than
25 years of therapy, prescription drugs, and
God knows how many Alcoholics Anonymous
meetings.*[1]

In my teaching career, I've been entrusted by many
students with intimate and sometimes painful personal
stories. I admire their courage. And I always honor their
privacy and our pact of confidentiality. Denise's story is,
beyond a doubt, the most heart-wrenching and inspiring story
I have ever had the privilege of listening to. Denise (not her
real name) not only agreed to share her story with me; she was
eager to share it with you in the hope that you, or someone
you know, will be served by it along the harrowing journey
through the dark night of the soul. Sometimes these healing
journeys take decades to complete. Denise did not even ask me
to use a fictitious name; I chose to out of concern for her
privacy.

Before we hear Denise's story, let's look at some sobering

research findings of the lifelong harm that accrues from
childhood trauma.

Adverse Childhood Experiences

Sexual abuse at the hands of an adult causes lifelong damage;
when inflicted by a parent, the damage leaves permanent scars.
Researchers from the Centers for Disease Control and
Prevention, and Kaiser Medical Center studied the long-term
effects on children who experienced one or more of the
following:

- Physical abuse
- Emotional abuse
- Sexual abuse
- Physical and/or emotional neglect
- Growing up in a household where a parent is mentally
  ill, substance-dependent, or incarcerated
- Growing up in a household where there's parental
  separation or divorce
- Growing up in a household where there's domestic
  violence

What this study showed is that children who suffer sexual
abuse, or physical violence, or severe neglect, or any other form
of adverse childhood experience, live troubled lives. In addition
to behavioral problems, many medical conditions also occur
more frequently:

> Compared to those who reported no ACE exposure, the
> adjusted odds of reporting myocardial infarction, asthma,
> fair/poor health, frequent mental distress, and disability were
> higher for those reporting one to three, four to six, or seven
> to nine ACEs. Odds of reporting coronary heart disease and

stroke were higher for those who reported four to six and seven to nine ACEs; odds of diabetes were higher for those reporting one to three and four to six ACEs.[2]

Dr. Nadine Burke Harris is the founder and CEO of the Center for Youth Wellness in San Francisco. In her book, *The Deepest Well: Healing the Long-Term Effects of Childhood Adversity*, she explains how early adversity, if experienced in high enough doses, *literally gets under our skin, changing people in ways that can endure in their bodies for decades [...] It can tip a child's developmental trajectory and affect physiology. It can trigger chronic inflammation and hormonal changes that can last a lifetime. It can alter the way DNA is read and how cells replicate, and it can dramatically increase the risk for heart disease, stroke, cancer, diabetes—even Alzheimer's.*[3]

Transformative Breathwork Cured Denise's PTSD

I cannot make this stuff up. I also know I am not up to the task of conveying Denise's story adequately. But you need to hear this, so I'm going to share the briefest version I can that will carry its import. Here is a timeline of Denise's life highlighting the most relevant events:

1. 3 years old: Sexually abused in her crib by her father
2. 6 years old: Denise's father hit her when she came home with a torn jacket pocket
3. 12 years old: Denise's mother was "unpredictable" and asked, "Do you think I'm an alcoholic?"
4. 16 years old: Raped by boyfriend; passed out when she stepped in front of class to give a report
5. 20-30 years old:
6. Raped by husband two weeks after giving birth; almost died from blood loss;

7. Backhanded by her husband just as her father had done;
8. leaves husband;
9. loses control of drinking–becomes an alcoholic;
10. husband kidnaps their two kids multiple times;
11. son nearly dies from complications of a burn incurred while staying with father that went untreated
12. 30-40 years old:
13. After her husband kidnapped their two children for the third time, Denise took them across the country to Taos, New Mexico. The three of them lived under a plastic tarp at a campground outside Taos for the first month before moving to a free camping spot in the mountains
14. 40-50 years old:
15. Having moved back east to Nyack, New York, Denise has been sober four years when she is raped by a newcomer to Alcoholics Anonymous after lending him $20
16. Denise suffers from extreme anxiety and is scared of talking to people, of leaving home, of driving (the world is VUCA, uncertain and unpredictable)
17. 50+ years old:
18. After extensive psychotherapy, prescription drugs, and 25 years of attending Alcoholics Anonymous meetings regularly, Denise is referred to Heather Davis by Dr. Rollow (both practice at the Kernan Medical Center outside of Baltimore, Maryland)

Breaking Through

I want my Mommy!, Denise blurted out during the fourth and final session of Transformational Breathwork. She doesn't remember much else from her sessions with Heather Davis, a breathworker trained by Jessica Dibb, founder of the Inspiration Community in Owings Mills, Maryland. But Denise remembers crying out for her mommy and she remembers the indescribable relief that followed. She describes this moment as a breakthrough, as the tipping point, as the watershed moment separating what life was like prior to it and what life has been like since:

> *Breathwork changed my life. After four sessions with Heather Davis, my PTSD was gone. After years and years of therapy. Ever since that day, I felt more like myself than I can remember ever feeling before. It was so powerful, Joe!*[4]

> -Denise

When Denise told me this, I asked her, *So that's why you looked at me that way when I shared my experience when I was back in my crib, the early childhood experience that preceded my 'bliss in the garden of Eden' experience in India?* She nodded yes.

Dissociation is the common thread connecting many maladies, many of our so-called mental health problems. Breath-centered practices re-associate the conscious mind with whatever events, experiences, and aspects of ourselves we have shut off. Only by reconnecting with these repressed, disowned parts of ourselves can we be 'born again' into whole, healthy, happy people.

Inquiry Question: What are you hiding from yourself?

BREATHING BRIDGES

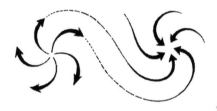

SIXTEEN

Introduction to Part 3

The lungs are placed in a recess so sacred and hidden that nature would seem to have specially withdrawn this part both from the eyes and from the intellect: for, beyond the wish, it has not yet been granted to any one to fit a window to the breast and redeem from darkness the profounder secrets of nature. For of all of the parts of the body, the lungs alone, as if shrinking from observation, cease from their movement and collapse at once on the first entrance of light and self-revelation. Hence such an ignorance of respiration and a sort of holy wonder. Still let me draw near to the inmost vitals, and concerning so obscure a matter, make at least a guess. [1]

In Part 1 we journeyed through the hellish landscape of VUCA-Dukkha, Distress-Disease; then in Part 2 we discussed inspiring examples of the effectiveness of breath-centered practices as a remedy for such things as anxiety, depression, weight, and even PTSD.

Here in Part 3, we delve deeply into the breathing system itself, and into its unique relationship with other systems of the body that accounts for the efficacy of breath-centered practices.

Why is breath so important?

Breath is widely regarded as the most important aspect of yoga praxis, despite the dominance of all the physical styles you may encounter today. Breath has traditionally been described as the bridge between the outer physical practices and the inner practices of meditation. Breath provides our outer conscious, willful, voluntary self access to the inner unconscious, instinctive, involuntary physiological processes.

Breathing rhythm is intrinsically linked with other physiological processes, such as heart rhythms. Changes in any of these rhythms alters the breath rhythm. What is crucial for our purpose is that consciously altering the breath rhythm will modulate the heart rhythm, brainwave rhythm, and so on. Therefore, breath provides the best way to manage stress states.

The respiratory system is unique because it, unlike all the other autonomic systems, affords both automatic and manual control. Breath has two separate control pathways—that's how breath can be completely automatic most of the time but, at will, brought under conscious control. This is the anatomical basis of all breathwork.

Iceberg - non-conscious vs. conscious control
of breathing

Conscious observation & control of breathing

Proprioception can be likened to an upside-down
periscope: one extends this periscope down into the
murky depths into the non-conscious body to sense
breathing, to feel its movements via movements of the

skin, belly, chest, etc. Although we have direct control over the diaphragm's movements, we can have no direct feedback from it. You cannot feel your diaphragm because all of the afferent nerves terminate in the lower parts of the brain, especially in the respiratory control center in the brainstem. The conscious mind has no access to this information. Thus, the diaphragm affords one a direct experience of the so-called mind/body split. Simultaneously, the diaphragm affords one an easy way to bridge it.

Non-conscious control of breathing

The respiratory center receives data from sensors:

- -chemical
- -electrical
- -mechanical (pressure), including direct feedback from the diaphragm
- -heart rate
- -HRV
- -blood pressure
- -oxygen saturation
- -carbon dioxide saturation
- -exchange rate from inside alveoli across membrane to blood stream

This data is not available to the conscious mind; therefore, you cannot sense the movements of the diaphragm directly. Only by the effects these movements have on what is around it, such as your belly and chest wall.

Breathing that is ordered and rhythmic dissolves stress. One of the most important ways ordered breathing dissolves stress is through sympathetic resonance with the rhythm of heartbeats; when this occurs your entire physiology starts to come into coherence, into rhythmic harmony. In other words, ordered breathing transforms dis-ease into ease.

SEVENTEEN

Why Breathe At All?

W henever I teach breathing, I always begin with anatomy because it's the easiest, most logical, most tangible aspect; the form and actions of the bones and muscles and connective tissues that make up your 'air pump' are *things*. Physiology, on the other hand, pertains largely to systems and their processes, which are *not* things. Therefore, physiology is a more abstract subject in comparison to anatomy.

But an even better place to begin is the why of breathing. What is the respiratory system's primary purpose? Does it serve other purposes as well?

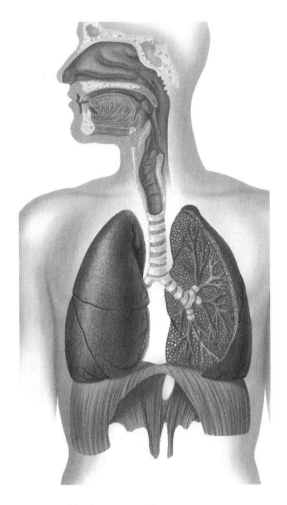

The human respiratory system

Purpose of the Respiratory System

The job of this air pump, technically, is respiratory ventilation —the biomechanics of moving air into and out of the lungs. But to understand why we breathe, we have to start at the other end of the process, inside the millions or billions of individual cells. For they are, so to speak, the breathing system's actual customers. It is the cells that require oxygen. It is their hunger for oxygen that drives the whole system.

Smoking Reduces Available Oxygen

Are you a smoker? Are you—or someone you know—trying to quit? One thing that helped me quit after failing for the umpteenth time, was understanding what carbon monoxide was doing to my body.

When carbon monoxide is breathed into the lungs, it binds with hemoglobin in red blood cells to make carboxyhemoglobin (COHb) which is then transported into the bloodstream. Once this happens, oxygen cannot bind with receptors on the same cell. And because CO is much faster at binding with hemoglobin than oxygen (about 200 times faster), when CO is present in the lungs, it wins the spot on red blood cells. This process diminishes the oxygen-carrying capacity in the bloodstream.

Carbon monoxide is quick to connect with red blood cells but is slow to exit the body, taking as much as a day to be exhaled through the lungs.

An abundance of carbon monoxide in the bloodstream starves the body of oxygen and in the worst cases, can cause death.[1]

Cellular respiration is the why of breathing

Cellular respiration is the chemical process that uses the oxygen to create energy required by every physiological process. Each inhale delivers oxygen to the cells and every exhale hauls away excess carbon dioxide and other waste products from the teeny-tiny energy plant within each cell.

Respiratory ventilation (breathing) is only one part of the supply chain. Transportation of oxygen and carbon dioxide between the lungs and the cells is carried out by the cardiovascular system. The importance of this partnership between breathing and the cardiovascular system—particularly the relationship between their rhythms—will become clear as we look at respiratory sinus arrhythmia, heart rate variability, sympathetic resonance, and coherence.

EIGHTEEN

A Most Common Miracle

*This half-breath you are breathing right now is a
measure of the quality of your life.*

Breath is a marvel to behold. The more I learn about breathing, the greater my appreciation, awe, and wonder at its complexity and ingenuity. By the end of this book—if you do the exercises—you will have a new relationship with your own breathing. You'll have a new relationship with your oldest and closest companion.

Unless and until you experience its essence, breathing is as common as dirt. I read somewhere that a mystic is a person who experiences the mundane, the ordinary, the prosaic in extraordinary ways. Take a stroll into the mystic's garden with me, if you please, to see just how extraordinary breath actually is!

Breath is a gift, a miracle, and a mystery that happens all by itself.

Do you want to savor your life, your time among the living? Of course you do. And because you do, you should know there's only a very narrow slice of time to savor this mystery called life —now! Of course, you must think about the past and prepare for the future. Thinking is part of the now as much as breathing. The present moment is all there is. Ever. And how long is this slice of time we call *The Now*?

One half-breath.

It's ironic, don't you think, that we spend most of our lives avoiding the present moment? I think life should be measured not by a few isolated moments—the ones that take our breath away—but rather by the moments we spend fully present to breathing, to savoring the present moment whether it be pleasant or painful.

Like snowflakes or fingerprints, our breathing system and functioning are basically the same in every body, yet no two people breathe exactly the same way. Like the currents of wind or water, the streams and patterns of breath change constantly. No two breaths are the same. This breath you are breathing right now will never be repeated. You cannot breathe the same breath twice.

How long will you breathe? Each creature's time among the living—as a member of this season's 'standing crop'—ticks by one breath at a time. This is all the time you have. Period. Some teachers have said there's even a definite, predetermined number of breaths allotted to each person at birth. If that is true, it is clearly to your benefit to breathe slower!

In point of fact, this companion was here first, seeing as breath started long before conscious developed—long before you, the you who has a name and a social and cultural identity ever emerged as the inhabitant, the owner of your body. The first thing the body does when it emerges from the mother is to take and inhale, and the last thing this body will do before it returns to mother Earth is exhale. Consciousness develops long after birth and ends at or before death.

672,768,000 Breaths

Two breaths—one inhale with no exhale preceding it and one exhale with no inhale following it—form the bookends to each life. Between these two breaths, we inspire and expire continuously. The first inhale at birth and the final exhale at death are like a pair bookends: between them lies your limited time, measured by these binary couplets: this is the poetic meter of a life. In the span of time between your first inhale at birth and your last exhale at death lies your life's story.

On average, a person at rest takes about 16 breaths per minute. This means we breathe about 960 breaths an hour, 23,040 breaths a day, 8,409,600 a year. Unless we get a lot of exercise. The person who lives to 80 will take about 672,768,000 breaths in a lifetime.

Life is measured by the breaths you breathe consciously—not by the number of breaths you take, nor by the moments that take your breath away. Actually, it's more like the half-breaths you breathe with conscious awareness, with presence. The span of time we call 'now,' the present moment, lasts only as long as one relaxed half-breath, according to D.N. Stern's research. Not even a full breath cycle.

Gratitude, One Half-Breath At A Time

This narrow window is all the time we ever have to be present, to be fully and consciously alive. In a very real way, the span of this one right-here and right-now half-breath you are taking now is the only time you have available to experience the mystery, privilege, and joy of being alive.

One day your breathing will end. One day, when and where you cannot know, you will breathe out and not breathe in again. Between this breath and that final breath, breathe deeply! Breathe! Gratitude for breath puts things in perspective. Most so-called problems fade in importance when death is remembered. Being aware that breath will not last forever fosters appreciation and gratitude.

Breathing gratitude (instructions)

Try it out right now:

Inhale. That exhale you just took, that preceded this inhale, is it part of this present moment or is it already a memory? And what about the exhale that is about to follow? This narrow window is all the time we ever have to be present, to be fully and consciously alive. If you're not present for this once-and-gone half-breath, you miss it. It's gone.

NINETEEN

The Respiratory Diaphragm

Your new relationship with breathing centers on the diaphragm. This new intimacy with your own diaphragm and its movements builds a bridge connecting you—the conscious, ego-defined you—to the rest of you. In yoga parlance, we call this connecting little self with BIG SELF. More about this later.

The word diaphragm breaks down into *dia-*, meaning apart from, and *phragm*, which is Latin for fence.

The respiratory diaphragm is among the most important muscles of the entire body because it is the primary muscle of breathing. The complex, intricate sequence of events that make up a single breath cycle involves many muscles, but none plays a larger role than the respiratory diaphragm. So why, you may be wondering, does its name refer to a fence? Because another function of the respiratory diaphragm is as a septum, a separator; it separates thorax (lungs and heart) from the abdomen (liver, stomach, and intestines).

Located at the base of the rib cage, it separates your chest cavity from the viscera within your belly. It forms the floor of the thorax (upper body, chest) and the roof of the abdomen (lower body, belly, and hips). The respiratory diaphragm serves as a barrier separating the liquid-filled compartment below, if you will, from the air-filled compartment above.

Did you know that some animals' lungs are below the diaphragm, instead of above it? Or that, despite the fact its diaphragm is like ours, a cow can function more or less normally with it paralyzed?

Form

The respiratory diaphragm is shaped like an umbrella with two handles

The respiratory diaphragm closely resembles an umbrella. Its main feature is a central dome of stiff tendinous fibers. At its outer edge, this thin, circular membrane merges with muscle fibers extending outward in every direction. These muscle fibers attach to the inside surfaces of the lowest ribs, and also to several spinal vertebrae. If you've ever been on a trampoline, you can picture these muscle fibers as the strong steel cables that attach the central membrane to the outer structure. Real umbrellas have one handle; the respiratory diaphragm has two. Called crura (from the Latin word crus, meaning leg-like), each crus muscle bundle extends down and attaches to lumbar vertebrae.

Movement

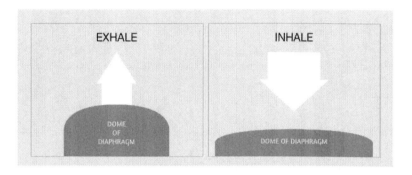

The respiratory diaphragm moves down on inhale and up on exhale.

Basically, your respiratory diaphragm initiates an inhale by contracting downward toward your feet; then it initiates the exhale by relaxing its contraction, by releasing the dome upward —back to the starting position. This piston-like movement inside the cylinder-like rib cage repeats, rhythmically, some 23,000 times each day. Does this number ring any bells?

It should, because it's exactly the same number as we saw in the last chapter for how many breaths the average person takes in a day. One breath cycle equals one down and up journey of your diaphragm. It's obvious once you think about it. But for some reason it's a minor leap to equate breath rate with diaphragm rate. So try to remember to substitute *diaphragm rate* wherever you see or hear *breath rate*, as in:

On average, a person's diaphragm travels up and down about 16 times per minute. This means about 960 diaphragm excursions each hour, 23,040 excursions a day, 8,409,600 excursions a year. Unless we get a lot of exercise. The diaphragm of a person who lives to 80 will take about 672,768,000 excursions in a lifetime.

This DIY model demonstrates how the diaphragm's downward movement (represented by pulling down on the green balloon) fills the lungs (inflates the red balloon) by reducing atmospheric pressure within the lungs.

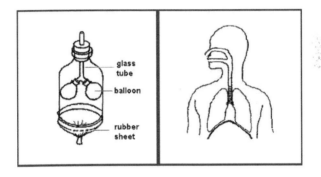

Respiratory Diaphragm (model with balloons inside bell jar)

Digestion & Acid Reflux

The diaphragm's rhythmic movements assist the peristaltic movements of the digestive tract. At least that's what happens when breathing is natural, unfettered by chronic stress. One of the side effects of holding your gut in (to look thinner), gut clenching and breath holding (to avert the impulse to flee or fight) may be acid reflux. Remember those two 'handles' on the umbrella, the two crural muscles? Well, they're not really part of the diaphragm at all. At a minimum, some researchers are now saying, the so-called crural diaphragm is an entirely different structure from the costal diaphragm, the part that attaches to the ribs.

Are you one of those unfortunate souls with acid reflux? Chronic chest breathing, where the belly and low ribs move little, if at all, not only inhibits your breathing, it also interferes with the normal functioning of your digestive tract. This is because the two 'legs' of the respiratory diaphragm have more to do with digestion than with breathing! In the diaphragm: two physiological muscles in one, the crural diaphragm is described as a *gastrointestinal sphincter [...] implicated strongly in [...] gastro-oesophageal reflux disease.*[1]

Posture & Movement

The muscles of the crural and costal diaphragms are part of an interconnected chain of muscles that work synergistically. Thomas Meyers, author of *Anatomy Trains*, calls the entire chain the *Deep Front Line*. The next downlink in this chain are the psoas and iliacus muscles, or iliopsoas for short. The crura, together with the psoas, stabilize posture. Thus, it should come as no shock to learn that both the psoas and diaphragm muscles clench under stressful conditions. They are integral to the fright, fight, or flee response. What is worse, chronic stress causes the transverse abdominis, iliopsoas, and diaphragm to become both tight and weak. So if you have the habit of shallow breathing or breath holding, your psoas muscle is affected and adds to the overall feeling of tightness. I think it not unreasonable to say acid reflux may result from tight and/or weak core muscles, the crural muscles in particular.

Inquiry Question: Where and what do I feel in my body that I name anxious, stressed out, threatened, tight? Do I stop breathing?

Evolutionary Advantage

The complete partition between the thoracic and abdominal parts of the celom [trunk] by the diaphragm can be considered a key evolutionary innovation for mammals. Once this partition has been completed, the characteristically mammalian pattern of aspiration breathing is established. Muscularization transformed the diaphragm into the principal force during inhalation. When the thoracic cavity became completely isolated as a unit by the muscular diaphragm, the functional demand of ventilating the elaborate airways could be satisfied by an energetically most efficient design. Inhalation, which takes place actively by contraction of the diaphragm, is followed by very efficient exhalation without muscular effort. Apparently the potential energy created by the contraction of the diaphragm is stored in the elastic tissues of the thoracic unit and the lung. This energy is released when lung and thorax recoil, causing exhalation. The maximal matching of form and functional demand of the mammalian design of lungs and breathing apparatus is further perfected by the coupling of breathing pattern with mode of locomotion.[2]

In its role as the primary muscle of respiration, your diaphragm is comparable to the pistons in an engine. Actually, a more apt comparison is to a turbocharger: certain breath techniques, such as Kapalabhati and Breath of Fire supercharge metabolism, raise body temperature, increase mental alacrity—and boost courage. Bellows Breath takes its name from the diaphragm's ability to 'fan the fire' in the belly. In fact, some claim that the Greek god, Hephaestus, later called Vulcan by the Romans, modeled the first bellows after his own diaphragm.

Breath-centered practices such as Diaphragmatic Breathing, Bhastrika (Bellows Breath), Kapalabhati (Skull Shining Breath), and Breath of Fire—as well as more athletic, movement-oriented practices that include synchronization of breath and action (e.g., Surya Namaskar)—have been practiced for thousands of years for their 'turbocharger' effects.

Equine Inspiration

The horse figures prominently in mythology as a symbol for breath. And for good reason. The way a horse's breathing synchronizes with its movement will inspire you to do likewise, whether in Sun Salutations, swimming, running, or simply walking.

> During canter of the horse, inhalation is coincident with the lifting of the lead forelimb. At this point, the horse leaves the ground and air flows into the lung. When the limbs return to the ground, the thoracic cage undergoes compressive loading. As the loading escalates, exhalation begins at a high rate. During the gallop, inhalation is confined to the offloaded interval when the horse is entirely off the ground or supported by the hind limbs only. As the first forelimb touches the ground, thoracic loading begins and exhalation starts. Phase-locking gait and respiration is clearly adaptive since increased demands for oxygen are met by increased ventilation automatically when the animal shifts from one mode of locomotion into the other. Such fine adaptive tuning of meeting varying functional demands is established by fortuitous mammalian thoracic design in which the thoracic complex is coupled mechanically in such a way as to enable phase-locking gait with respiration.[3]

In plain English, the power and endurance of the horse can be attributed to the evolution of a breathing system that takes advantage of its own movement to turbocharge ventilation. It leaps into the air to not only move forward but also to inhale, and it uses the impact of landing to augment exhale. Brilliant!

What is my diaphragm rate? (instructions)

Repeat the previous exercise where you counted exhales, but this time count diaphragm movements instead. Count each up and down circuit as one diaphragm cycle for two minutes and then divide that number in half to arrive at an average. The sole difference from the previous exercise is that you are focusing on the physical movements of your diaphragm rather than on the abstract notion of a breath cycle.

TWENTY

Your Bridge to Breath-Centered Practices

The breath is the intersection of the body and mind. Take a deep breath to bring your mind back to your body.

Thich Nhat Hanh

Andrew Weil calls breathing the master key to vitality; I call the diaphragm the master key to breath-centered practices. I should clarify, before going any further, that whenever the word diaphragm is mentioned without qualification I am speaking of the respiratory diaphragm. There are actually three major diaphragms we talk about, the other two being the pelvic and vocal diaphragms. But wherever you encounter the word without qualification you can assume we are speaking of the respiratory diaphragm.

Inquiry Question: What is my experience of my diaphragm?

Working Knowledge

Luckily for us, the diaphragm is the one thing you need working knowledge of to get started. Getting to know your diaphragm gives you a head start toward reaping the rewards of breathwork. The respiratory diaphragm is your 'invisible friend,' your constant companion. When you breathe in accordance with how the respiratory system is meant to work, everything else follows behind the diaphragm's lead. You don't need anything else, at least not in the beginning.

What do we mean by working knowledge? Let's use the analogy of driving. Millions and millions of people drive each day without understanding all that goes on under the hood, without understanding details of how an internal combustion engine works or how all the other components and systems work. Yet they drive perfectly. They go from point A to point B with no problem. So, if you drive a car, you have a working knowledge of cars.

In breath-centered practices, you need working knowledge of your own diaphragm. You do not need to know all its complexities. I mean, many people have studied just the diaphragm their entire lives without understanding it completely. You need to know where your diaphragm is, how it is supposed to initiate and coordinate the entire process of breathing, and how to help it do its job better.

Whereas academic knowledge of anatomy and physiology tends to be second-hand, tends to be divorced from experience, breath-centered practices require first-hand knowledge, the kind you can only get from direct experience.

Take ample time now and do the following inquiry; it will help you get acquainted with the star of the show, the most important bridge for all breath-centered practices: your respiratory diaphragm.

Befriend Your Diaphragm (instructions)

1. Using your fingertips, locate the bottom of your rib cage. It may be easier to start in the middle of your chest, below the nipples, where the dagger-shaped sternum bone tapers to a point. From this point, walk your fingers in opposite directions as you trace the boundary separating hard and bony above from soft and fleshy below.
2. As you proceed outward, palpate (press inward in order to 'read' what your fingertips find inside) as you go. Where your fingers need to go is not deep, but rather just a fraction of an inch.
3. What you're feeling for is the backside of the hard edge. You should be able to trace the bottom edge of diaphragm's central umbrella-shaped dome, at least at two or three spots. This is the diaphragm's outer rim; its muscle fibers attach to the inside surface of your ribs all the way around.

Location of the respiratory diaphragm

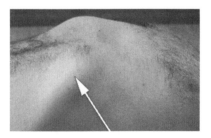

TIP: Imagine your fingers doing this around an umbrella; if you have one handy, practice on it first.

TIP: Spend as much time as you need to locate your diaphragm and feel how it moves before proceeding to the next section.

The Bridge To No-where, Now-here

When you did the "Locate Your Diaphragm" inquiry, did you notice that the only thing you can actually palpate is its outer edge, where it's attached underneath your ribs? But even that's vague. The plain fact is, you have no direct sensation of the diaphragm. There are no sensory nerves in it like those in your skin, or your mouth, or your fingers. Actually, there are plenty of sensory nerves. But they all terminate in the lower parts of your brain, affording no conscious awareness of them.

Therefore, you can only infer the diaphragm and its movements by changes to the organs and bones it causes to move. Bottom line, when it comes to the diaphragm, there simply is no possibility of direct experience. This means that the one concrete piece of physical anatomy you need a good working knowledge of cannot be felt or seen, ever!

Welcome to the Mind/Body Disconnect

And that's perfect, for the diaphragm represents the direct access to the intangible. The inner body, as it's called in yoga.

Now, this directly contradicts what I always say about the importance, the necessity even, of direct experience. One of the basic ironies of breathwork is that while the respiratory diaphragm is the prime mover of breath, you can only know it indirectly, by how it changes the shape of things around it. As you become more intimately acquainted with the diaphragm, you will develop greater sensitivity to it, but you can never know it directly.

Repeat the *Locate Your Diaphragm* inquiry, if you will. This time, imagine the diaphragm is an invisible friend leaning against the inside wall of your ribs. Imagine it senses your presence, too, but also cannot contact you directly. Be open and playful to intuiting the stranger on the other side of this impenetrable wall sensing your presence exactly as you are intuiting its presence.

There's something paradoxical about the fact that the diaphragm, the prime mover of breath, cannot be seen or directly felt. We have to infer its movements from the effects it has on the surrounding structures, such as the belly and the ribs. Likewise, prana—otherwise known as the life force, Chi, or bioelectric energy—cannot be directly perceived. We only know prana by its manifestations, just as we can only 'see' the wind by the movements of leaves in the trees. If the notion of prana seems vague or mysterious, it may have something to do with the fact that you can't even perceive the movements of your own diaphragm directly.

In the end, it's a paradox: the diaphragm is the bridge that connects mind and body, and yet it's also the impassable chasm separating the knowable, so-called outer body from the unknowable, so-called inner body.

TWENTY-ONE

The Heart's Little Helper

Breathing itself acts to raise and lower blood pressure, resulting in the respiratory arterial pressure wave which rises and falls with exhalation and inhalation, respectively.[1]

Stephen Elliott

In addition to its primary function as an air pump, the respiratory diaphragm also functions as an accessory to the heart in pumping blood throughout the entire body. That's why the diaphragm is referred to as a 'second heart' and why the respiratory and cardiovascular systems are increasingly referred to as the cardiopulmonary system. Simply stated, blood pressure increases during exhale and decreases during inhale.

Optimal vs. Suboptimal Breathing

Among the primary causes of chronically-elevated blood pressure is what Elliott calls *suboptimal breathing*. What is suboptimal breathing? Suboptimal breathing is any breath rate and depth and rhythm that does not help the heart pump blood. Usually, this includes breathing faster than around five or six breaths per minute and, consequently, breathing a smaller volume of air with each breath cycle. Suboptimal breathing makes the heart work harder and faster. Heart rate increases. Blood pressure increases. If you recall from our previous discussion of vital signs, the official 'normal' breathing rate is 15 breaths per minute. So, our accepted norm is far from optimal! And it is my pet theory that average breath rates are climbing in tandem with the accelerating worldwide epidemic of hypertension.

Optimal breathing, on the other hand, helps the heart pump blood—and reduces the amount of work the heart has to do. Parallel to respiratory sinus arrhythmia, which is the speeding up of heartbeats during inhale and the slowing down of heartbeats during exhale, blood pressure rises and falls. Elliott calls this phenomenon the *respiratory arterial pressure wave:*

> Inhalation results in a strong negative thoracic pressure (a vacuum) resulting in expansion of the lungs and the inflow of air from the external environment. Simultaneously, this internal pressure differential causes blood vessels in the chest to expand. Because the chest is replete with blood vessels, this results in significant "storage" of blood in the chest during inhalation, thereby reducing blood flow returning to the heart, lowering heart output and arterial pressure. [6] The opposite occurs during exhalation. In this way, breathing itself acts to raise and lower blood pressure, resulting in the respiratory arterial pressure wave which rises and falls with exhalation and inhalation, respectively.

[...]

Calling on Medical Physiology, during rest, the 5% variation in heartbeat rate corresponds to an arterial pressure change of 4 to 6 mmHg (millimeters of mercury); during deep respiration, the 30% variation in heartbeat rate corresponds to changes in arterial pressure of up to 20 mmHg.[2]

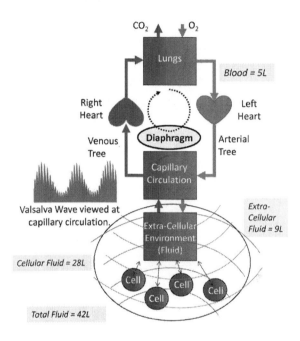

Mechanics of Cardiopulmonary Resonance - Schematic View.
Copyright: Stephen Elliott 2018. Used with permission.

TWENTY-TWO

Bridge Over Troubled Wires

There is a very direct relationship between breath rate, mood state, and autonomic nervous system state.[1]

Sat Bir Singh Khalsa

P art of the wonder of life on this planet, and particularly of human evolution, is the automation of our life support systems. The autonomic nervous system (ANS) regulates every aspect of breathing without requiring you to be consciously involved. That's a very good thing! If you had to remember to breathe every time, you would never have time to do anything else!

As human life accelerates—becomes faster, more demanding, more taxing—stress increases in equal measure. Rapid breathing and breathlessness are symptoms of a distressed, out-of-whack autonomic nervous system. Such imbalances, when chronic, lie at the heart of insomnia, hypertension, anxiety, depression, and many other so-called lifestyle diseases.

Nine times out of ten the sympathetic (SNS) branch of the ANS is the culprit; it stays super-charged and hogs the stage. In plain English, the tone of the SNS is too high too often and for too long at a time. Andrew Weil claims chronic stress is the root cause of lifestyle diseases such as hypertension, anxiety, depression, insomnia, obesity, irritable bowel syndrome, and immune-system problems. He singles out chronic activation of the sympathetic nervous system as the main culprit and, further, flatly claims breathwork "is our only chance to influence the autonomic nervous system."

Meanwhile, the poor parasympathetic (PSNS) branch gets shoved off-stage, leaving it insufficient time to play its role in the body's daily cycle of activity-rest, procure-assimilate, and the like. Assimilation includes more than the digestion of food, by the way; sleep is when you assimilate all the sensory impressions taken in during waking hours. Without this mental 'digestion,' cognitive performance suffers the next day.

Stress, Breath, and the Autonomic Nervous System

Breath is the missing link in the chain of mind, brain, autonomic nervous system (ANS), and the body in distress. When order is restored to breathing, order follows in the ANS; parasympathetic tone increases to match the tone of the sympathetic, as the following graph shows:

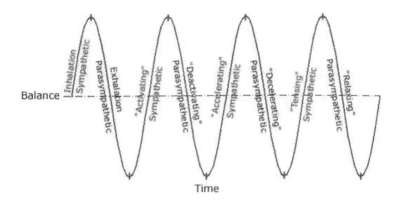

Respiratory Sinus Arrhythmia: the sympathetic nervous
system is activated by inhaling, while the parasympathetic
nervous system is activated by exhaling

One of the numerous studies on how this works concludes that *engaging in controlled breathing [has] been shown to enhance SNS [sympathetic nervous system] control during stress.* Specifically, down-regulation of the SNS is greatest when breathing is slow and deep, at a rate of four breaths per minute, and when emphasis is placed—when more of the breath cycle is devoted to—the span between mid-inhale and mid-exhale. This is valuable data since SNS overstimulation is rampant and constitutes the number one culprit in so many of our modern 'lifestyle' diseases.

Slowing down your breathing and taking a few deep breaths is oftentimes all it takes to restore homeostasis. Even merely focusing attention in a sustained, intentional manner—without changing breath pattern at all—can do the trick.

Don't think of it as interfering. Think of it as intervening on behalf of your health and sanity. You don't even need to slow it down because, as scientific research studies have demonstrated, merely focusing attention on breathing slows it down —automagically!

If, on top of that, you want not merely to survive but to thrive, well, then, learning the practices provided in this book will be of tremendous help. Breath is the only easily-accessed bridge to the autonomic nervous system (ANS) available to us, the one and only direct access to cultivating homeodynamic balance. Through these practices, you will rewire your electrical circuits and rewrite that song of troubled wires into (to paraphrase Plato) a love song sung among all the organs of your body.

Not only will these techniques help you manage whatever stress you have now, but they also increase your ability to perform under the increased levels of stress that come with success.

Breath-centered practices deactivate the stress response. And they do so within moments, typically. And do I need to say again that they are free?

Inquiry Question: Is my jaw relaxed or clenched as I breathe this one half-breath? Is clenching my jaw interfering with taking a relaxed breath?

TWENTY-THREE

From Chaos to Coherence

Incoherence

Ironically, it's easier to define incoherence than coherence. In matters of personal taste, liking a thing indicates it is, at least for you, coherent; we tend to dislike incoherence. We all know what incoherent speech is—at least we know it when we hear it. We can tell the difference between noise and music, although the listener next to you may disagree. We may not know much about art but we know what we like. This is more than a mere whim because your gut brain is ancient and wise. The enteric nervous system evolved long before that interloper, the second brain located up inside your head. Your stomach knows what is good to eat and what is poisonous—up to a point anyway. All I'm saying is that, as a very general rule of thumb, coherence is wholesome and incoherence is not.

Have you experienced unexpected air turbulence during an airline flight? I certainly have, although not as extreme as described by this passenger:

My worst flight was on a trip from Dublin to London. Out of nowhere, the plane took a nosedive ... for about eight seconds! I know it doesn't seem like that long, but seriously, count for eight seconds. That's a long nose dive! Passengers started screaming, luggage went flying out of the overhead bins and the lights went out. So scary! I really thought the plane was going to crash. Everything ended up being okay, at least I think so. The pilot never even announced what happened.[1]

This is a perfect description of the effects of incoherence on the body and mind. Just reading it is enough to cause distress, the emotional turbulence we feel under psycho-physiological incoherence. The resulting turbulence can show up as physical, emotional, cognitive, or spiritual distress. In the neuroendocrine system, for example, stress activates the pituitary-adrenal axis, causing a two- to five-fold increase in blood plasma levels of adrenocorticotropin (ACTH), 8-lipotropin and 3-endorphin.*[2]

What does incoherence feel like? It's that inner turbulence we feel whenever our different systems fall out of harmony, out of phase—when they rub each other the wrong way. Turbulence is incoherence and incoherence is distress—in a word, dukkha. Stress is shorthand for the experience of incoherence.

Coherence

What, then, is coherence? We'll begin with the dictionary definitions, as I do out of habit.

Definition of coherent:

- The quality of being logical and consistent. Example:

This raises further questions on the coherence of state policy.

- The quality of forming a unified whole. Example: *The group began to lose coherence and the artists took separate directions.*

Synonyms: logical, good sense, understandable, soundness, organized, orderly, unified, rational, intelligible.

Antonyms: confused, disorderly, irrational, unintelligible, unsystematic, disorganized, incoherent, noncoherent.

The dictionary definition of coherence is all well and good, yet when it comes to the kind of coherence we are talking about this is equivalent to swallowing an ocean just to sample seawater. What I mean is, coherence is a huge subject, one we could easily drown in. So, with a high-level definition in hand, let's narrow our topic down.

Each system, whether respiratory, cardiovascular, digestive, nervous, et al., has its own rhythm, its own speed, its own frequency it oscillates to. The coherence we are talking about is the kind Plato described in his famous dictum: "Health is a consummated love affair among the organs of the body." In other words, optimal health is what you get when coherence holds sway within and among the systems of the body, mind, and spirit. Coherence, when applied to the internal milieu of the body, mind, and spirit, is a one-word summation of Plato's *"consummated love affair"*.

TWENTY-FOUR

Mindset (Words Matter!)

Words matter. A lot. As in *loose lips sink ships.*

A person can be labeled a terrorist or a martyr, depending on the speaker's politics, nationality, allegiance–his of her *worldview*. Which is correct? Likewise, the name given to a condition or disease by the individual who discovers or invents it can end up causing not just misunderstanding; misnomers can cause long-lasting harm.

People are motivated less by facts than by feelings. Have you heard the news? "Post-truth" has been declared Word of the Year by Oxford Dictionary[1]. In a nutshell, post-truth means facts matter less than mindset. In a world where so many base their actions more on pseudo-news outlets, talk radio, and other virtual echo chambers, conviction trumps fact.

Do you know that your mood can literally change the colors you see: mood state influences how incoming signals are processed inside your brain?

...emotions routinely affect how and what we see. Fear, for

example, can affect low-level visual processes, sad moods can alter susceptibility to visual illusions, and goal-directed desires can change the apparent size of goal-relevant objects. In addition, the layout of the physical environment, including the apparent steepness of a hill and the distance to the ground from a balcony can both be affected by emotional states.[2]

In some cases, what we call a thing can be so erroneous, so misleading, it 'infects' our reaction. The fact of the matter is, a rose by another name does not necessarily smell as sweet!

Trivia Question: When is a heart arrhythmia—a fluctuating heart rate —good news rather than bad news? *

Is this glass half empty or half full? The answer is relative; it depends on your desire, not on the facts. The truth is, the glass is always full!

Ludwig's Error (Respiratory Sinus Arrhythmia)

Oh, if only I had a Trekkie transporter! I'd beam back to 1846, grab the quill from Charles Ludwig[3] and stop him from incorrectly naming the healthy variations of heart rate *respiratory sinus arrhythmia*. With that one little stroke of the quill, I'd bend the needle of history and save the world. Well, at least save Carol from an anxiety attack over the idea.

Worry writ large, a long-time student confided last week at the end of class:

> *My ticker's out of whack. My doctor says its arrhythmia," Carol confided. Pausing just long enough to punctuate the news with a*

heavy sigh, she continued: "My heart races every time I breathe in and then slows down again when I exhale. Like a roller coaster, only no fun.

My initial concern now turned to curiosity. Carol always seemed a bit of a hypochondriac. I asked her to sit a moment and tell me all about it.

To make a long story short, I quickly realized Carol had misunderstood. Rather than some terrible disease, her doctor was trying to explain respiratory sinus arrhythmia, or RSA, which is perfectly normal. RSA describes how heartbeats are closer together in time during inhale and further apart during exhale. It actually indicates your heart and your breathing are 'dancing' together in sync, the way they're supposed to. Like many people would, Carol had simply assumed arrhythmic is bad.

Maybe, just maybe, Carol's doctor was simply trying to educate her—because he wanted her to understand that having respiratory sinus arrhythmia is good, whereas not having it is an indication of stress, or worse.

Contrary to how it sounds, respiratory sinus arrhythmia describes the heart's normal acceleration during inhalation and deceleration during exhalation.

> Because it is relatively uncommon to observe this pattern in most persons, medicine erroneously called it respiratory sinus arrhythmia (RSA). It is in no sense of the word an indication of a disorder. In fact, it is most pronounced in children (before they learn to breathe with their chest), in athletes, and in persons who have learned slow, abdominal breathing.[4]

Respiratory sinus arrhythmia, or RSA, is a terrible, incorrect term. This natural fluctuation may not be clock-like, may not adhere to the ideal of a metronome, but that does not mean it is arrhythmic. Unless your notion of rhythm is delimited by military marches and goose-stepping boots all marching to the same drumbeat.

Transforming Noise Into Music, One Ear At A Time

Sonny Rollins' music was way over my head the first time I heard *On Green Dolphin Street*. *You actually like this? It's just noise–makes no sense to me,* I said as I handed it back to Ray Wise, my mentor in all things jazz. Some weeks later I asked Ray if I could borrow it again after listening to lots of Charlie Parker, Dizzy Gillespie–and above all Thelonious Monk. Only then could my ears actually begin to hear and appreciate what Sonny Rollins was doing. I was fascinated by what seemed like the gradual, then sudden, emergence of order out of chaos as the gray stuff between my ears evolved, as my capacity to hear the obvious order in what previously seemed chaotic grew.

I had to go through the same process with Mozart's music before I could appreciate it. But instead of being confused, I found Mozart boring. Then one day my art history professor, Frank Russell, made an offhand remark that made me listen differently. Russell said, *Mozart is sublime, glorious–if you can get into what's he's doing.* It was delivered as a challenge, a sort of gauntlet laid at the feet of those in the class too desensitized by rock music to even attempt to take classical music seriously.

> The biggest myth about Mozart, is that his music is pure, joyous, and "easy". It is intense, dense, complex and has many layers. Joy and clarity is certainly only one of them, and often deceptive. To focus the attention only on that layer

make us miss his very human and quite mysterious complexity.[5]

Nowadays, I find listening to one of Mozart's late symphonies to be vivifying! I love the kaleidoscopic rhythms and patterns. I play Mozart now because I find that it stimulates and soothes me at the same time. I now find it hard to believe that so many early listeners thought it was noise, thought it was *arrhythmic.* As Dr. Robert Greenberg, American composer, pianist, musicologist, explains, *music that we turn to today for its lyricism and for the solace it offers from our overly complex world was considered by many of Mozart's contemporaries to be too long, too "academic," and unnecessarily complex.*[6]

In summary, whether a given phenomenon is rhythmic or arrhythmic is determined within the brain. Ludwig's brain misunderstood the healthy variations of heart rate to be unhealthy; unfortunately, we are still burdened with his error. Whereas Hans Selye realized his error in naming his discovery *The Stress Response*, albeit too late to replace it with *The General Adaptation Syndrome*, Charles Ludwig never did.

So, why did Ludwig call it an arrhythmia in the first place? Here's my best guess: in those glory days of the machine age, anything that ran *like clockwork*, that repeated with an unwavering frequency the way a clock does, is good. Anything irregular, anything arrhythmic, is obviously not working as it should. Ludwig simply lumped this natural variance in heart rate together with all the variances that actually are bad. He simply failed to see the difference. Thus, the only good heart is a clockwork heart. To my mind, it took complexity theory to explain the subtleties of the heart's apparent arrhythmia and to reframe them in the new term *heart rate variability*.

*Answer: Every time you take a breath: respiratory sinus arrhythmia, or RSA, is the (misleading) term describing the natural-and-normal acceleration and deceleration of heart rate within each breath cycle. RSA describes the acceleration during inhale and deceleration during exhale of heart rate (HR). The time intervals between individual contractions of the heart muscle decrease during inhale and increase during exhale, as shown in this illustration:

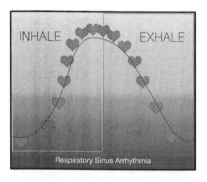

Respiratory Sinus Arrhythmia (RSA)

TWENTY-FIVE

Sympathetic Resonance

The cardiorespiratory control system can be viewed as one functional unit as it pursues the common aim of providing the tissues with oxygen, nutrients, protective agents, and a means of removing waste by-products.[1]

Feldman and Ellenberger

One of my goals in this book is to show you just how interdependent breathing and heart function are, despite being treated as separate by most medical professionals. Another is to teach you to use conscious breathing as the central physiological rhythm to entrain all the others, the same way the conductor uses his baton to entrain every player in the orchestra. We begin by synchronizing the heart rhythm to the breathing rhythm to create a physiological state of coherence or homeodynamic balance. Eventually, this coherence extends to every aspect of your body, breathing, physiology, brain, mind, emotion, soul, and spirit.

Breath-centered practices take advantage of the human respiratory system's dual control circuits, one automatic and unconscious, the other voluntary and conscious. Perhaps you've heard a yoga teacher say, "The mind is like a kite, and breath is the string that guides it." Yogis have long known that breathing rhythms act like a symphony conductor's baton, to synchronize and entrain other physiological systems, including the mind, into a coherent ensemble.

Yogis have long proclaimed breath the master key to unlocking health and vitality. And much, much more. As usual, we are finally coming around to their wisdom as technology affords direct measurements.

Breathwork is the master key to cardiopulmonary resonance–and overall psychophysical coherence–for one simple reason: changing your breathing changes the state of your autonomic nervous system (ANS).

When breath rate matches the heart's resonant frequency, as in Coherent Breathing™, it exerts the greatest influence. The heart responds because of a basic principle of physics: sympathetic resonance.

Your eyes may be glossing over because this is getting technical and nerdy. Stay with me. Why? Because the principle of sympathetic resonance informs your everyday life in ways that may surprise you.

Trivia Question:

- What's the secret of The Secret?
- Why do birds of a feather flock together?

- What explains the urge to circle the wagons, shut out any news or views that conflict with your own, and stick your head in the echo chamber?

Answer: Sympathetic Resonance.

The New Science of Breath

In 2013, while perusing the shelves of a bookstore at the Kripalu Center for Yoga & Health in Lennox, Massachusetts, I discovered *The New Science of Breathing* by Stephen Elliott[2]. This book has influenced my practice, teaching, and—most importantly—the content of this book. In it, Elliott explains coherence, the dynamic dance between heart and breath. Since that time, I have come to regard breathing and heart function as one system: the cardiopulmonary system. And the best way to gauge whether or not they are working together in harmony is by measuring heart rate variability, or HRV.

Not until I read *The New Science of Breath* did I begin to fathom the dynamic interplay between breathing pattern and heart rhythm. And I'd already studied breathing for decades. Therefore I assume what you are about to learn will come as news to you, as it did to me. I knew changing the pattern of breathing changes the relative tone of the branches of the autonomic nervous system, but I did not know it also changes heart rhythm. It does.

Recent advances in medical research have demonstrated the beneficial effects on heart rhythm caused by *Coherent Breathing*[TM] and other techniques. *Coherent Breathing*[TM] is both a basic, universal technique and a trademark. The only reason I am able to use it here is because Stephen Elliott generously allowed it. As an adjunct to *Coherent Breathing*^{TM}, Elliott also recommends a progressive muscle relaxation method he calls *The Six Bridges*.

For more information about *Coherent Breathing*^{TM}, *The Six Bridges*, as well as about Elliott's *Valsalva Wave Pro* biofeedback device, I recommend a visit to Stephen Elliott's COHERENCE website. While there, please check out (and purchase!) *Coherent Breathing Symphony*; my colleague Ty Ford and I created it to provide instruction and a musical practice aid for your benefit.

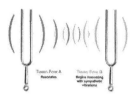

Sympathetic Resonance (tuning forks)

When you practice Coherent Breathing^{TM}, you create sympathetic resonance between breath rate—specifically, the frequency of diaphragm movements—and the frequency of heartbeats.

Harmonic Resonance

But, you may be wondering, breath rate and heart rate are nowhere near being equal; the two systems have very different rhythms. The norm for a healthy heart is 60 to 70 times per minute, while the norm for breathing rate, at 12-16 cycles per minute, is about one-fifth of that.

In the figure below, notice how the peaks of the breath cycles and the heartbeats line up perfectly. Each breath cycle (from one peak to the next) contains exactly three heartbeats. This means the breathing rhythm and the heart rhythm are *in phase* with one another. In other words, they are in coherence.

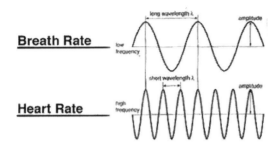

Breath and Heart Rhythms In Phase: The top wave represents one breath cycle and the bottom wave represents heartbeats. This synchronization is known as sympathetic resonance, and only occurs when you breathe at the heart's natural fundamental frequency– approximately five breaths per minute.

TWENTY-SIX

Heart Rate Variability

Remember Dr. Fried's patient—the one who halted the progression of his escalating blood pressure before it turned into full-blown hypertension? In the following fictional scenario, we'll look in on Victor before he meets Dr. Fried, as his vitals are being taken by a nurse.

Inspecting the elastic band stretched around his lower ribs, Victor says,

> *I can't recall anyone ever taking so many measurements of my breathing before.*

The nurse explains,

> *You wouldn't have unless you've been to a respiratory therapist. We include them here because Dr. Fried believes breathing is the key ingredient in health. He calls it the missing link. He left his lucrative practice as a surgeon because he believes breath retraining, plus other lifestyle changes, can prevent the need for prescription medications or surgery down the road. He says he'd*

rather help people create their own health. Other doctors think he's a bit radical, but I've seen some pretty amazing results in the three and a half years I've been here. That's why we teach every person who walks in the door how to breathe.

Victor asks,

What's this clip on my ear for? What's it measuring?

The nurse replies,

HRV.

Victor:

HRV?

Nurse:

Heart rate variability. The variations in heart rate. The gaps between one heartbeat and the next. Like this…

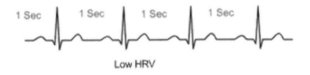

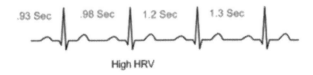

Your heart is not meant to beat at an unchanging pace like a metronome or mechanical clock. Heart rate naturally speeds up

during each inhale and slows down during each exhale. This is respiratory sinus arrhythmia (RSA). In fact, stress reduces HRV, resulting in less speeding up and slowing down of heart beats. In practice, HRV affords quick diagnosis of stress. Anyone with consistently low HRV probably also has chronic hypertension. Diaphragmatic Breathing, Coherent Breathing™, and other breathing techniques reestablish normal RSA and HRV. That's how they will help you avert full-blown hypertension.

Before Victor could ask another question, the nurse motions toward the hall:

All done. Follow me, please. The doctor will see you now.

In recent years, heart rate variability (HRV) has emerged as an important indicator of overall pulmonary-cardiovascular health. Further, many experts now consider HRV the best indicator of fitness and general health. Out of all the vital signs and other physiological measures, HRV is the single most reliable way to gauge whether your breathing and your heart are in sync. Coherent Breathing™ can generate up to a tenfold increase in heart rate variability.[1]

You don't need to understand all the physics and the math behind coherence to reap the benefits; however, understanding the basis of it–even if only a little bit–will likely make a lasting impression that will motivate you in your own practice.

All You Need Is HRV!

Luckily, there are now biofeedback devices, both wearable and affordable, that will tell you whether your breathing pattern and your heart rhythm are in sync–in real time. In 2015, I attended a 2-day conference at the Smithsonian Institute in Washington, D.C. called *Yoga as Medicine*. I was writing a research paper on the effectiveness of Activity Trackers and Social Media for people trying to lose weight. I wanted to see if technology could help with breathwork. I was looking for something wearable, inexpensive, and simple to use. The best device I'd tried so far was a FitBit bracelet. I wanted a device that would measure more than steps.

After a breakout session on *Mobile EEG and Yoga in Everyday Life,* I asked the presenter, Neilly Buckalew, of the University of Pittsburgh, for a recommendation on what EEG device I should purchase. The $700 headband she demonstrated looked much better than my EEG monitor gathering dust at home I'd spent a lot more on. Ms. Buckalew asked what I wanted out of using such a device. I cannot remember exactly what my reply was other than something vague about breath and meditation, but I do remember being surprised by her answer:

> *HRV is the best measure when your goal is primarily personal health, wellness, vitality and meditation. Heart rate variability is all you need to measure. You really don't need expensive EEG equipment. Just HRV!*

Here's the take-away: Heart rate variability is the best indicator of overall synchronization among the different rhythms that together constitute not only your organ systems but the whole of you—body, heart, mind, and spirit.

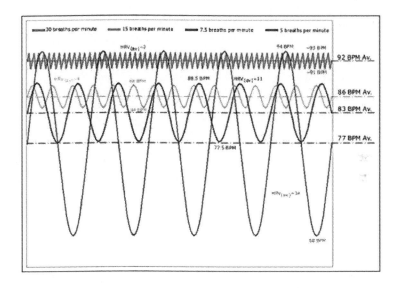

Heart Rate Variability (HRV) at 30, 15, 7.5, and 5 breaths per minute (Br/Min)

Coherent Breathing™ and similar techniques can reestablish normal RSA and HRV and, thereby, reverse the trend toward serious heart trouble. The graph below, from The New Science of Breath, clearly conveys the immediate benefits of breathing slowly. Compare the breath rates along the right edge against the corresponding heart rates and heart rate variability:

- 30: At a rate of thirty breaths per minute (30 BrPM), the average heart rate (HR) is 92 beats per minute (92 BPM); the variation in heart rate (HRV) is only 3– from a maximum of 93.5 BPM to a minimum of 90.5 BPM.
- 15: At fifteen breaths per minute (15 BrPM) the average heart rate drops to 86 BPM; HRV increases to 4–from 88 down to 84.
- 7.5: At seven and a half breaths per minute (7.5 BrPM) heart rate averages 83 BPM; HRV increases to 11
- 5: At five breaths per minute (5 BrPM), heart rate drops to an average of 77 BPM; heart rate variability (HRV) increases to 34

Simply slowing down your breath rate from 30 breaths per minute to 5 breaths per minute generates both a dramatic *decrease* in heart rate and a tenfold *increase* in heart rate variability–from an unhealthy heart rate variability of 3 heartbeats per minute to a health-promoting heart rate variability of 30!

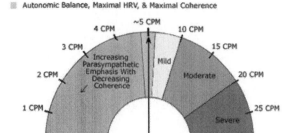

Autonomic Balance, Maximal HRV, and Maximal
Coherence

DIY Coherence

If tire misalignment shows up as your car's front end shaking, you'd take your car to a mechanic. But if incoherence shows up as stress in your body/mind, you don't need to visit a doctor, chiropractor, or massage therapist. You can easily bring yourself into coherence by practicing a simple breathing technique: Coherent Breathing™.

The end result? Optimal functioning of your entire system! Coherence. In a word, health—which Plato described as a "consummated love affair among the organs and systems of the body." Just a few minutes' practice of Coherent Breathing™ down-regulates the fight-or-flight response and increases the parasympathetic nervous system's rest-and-digest response. This is what Dr. Herbert Benson calls *The Relaxation Response.*

Practicing Coherent Breathing™ for just a few minutes creates feelings of calm serenity, balance, vitality, and joy! Feel free to jump straight to chapter 36, Coherent Breathing Symphony, to create your coherence right now!

GETTING STARTED WITH BREATH-CENTERED PRACTICES

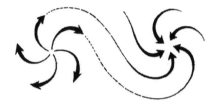

TWENTY-SEVEN

Introduction to Part 4: The Breath Within The Breath

Throughout human history, breath has enjoyed a place of honor, for breath and spirit are indelibly bound together. It's easy to see why breath would be thought of as spirit, for they 'leave' the body together at the moment of death. When inspiration fails to follow an expiration, spirit departs with it. This is why breathing has always been seen to be the vehicle for the body's animating spirit.

In many languages, the word for breath is also the word for spirit. From the Latin word *spiritus*, spirit means soul, courage, and vigor—and breath. The Greek word *pneuma* means motile air, spirit—and breath. In Greek, *psyche* (from which our modern word psychology originated) is the soul—and breath. In Hebrew, *ruach* is wind, or spirit—and breath as a vehicle of both divine inspiration and divine voice. In each case, breath is equated with spirit. Therefore, breathwork has long been regarded as a doorway to spiritual experience.

Today we may regard such metaphysical notions as childish; we have too much factual knowledge of the physiological workings of breath to subscribe to such antiquated beliefs. Thus, breathing is reduced to mere mechanics: ventilation, gas exchange, and cellular respiration. Don't get me wrong: I love studying anatomy and physiology. I also love reading scientific articles in peer-reviewed academic journals for their clarity and precision.

But we lost something valuable along the way. Over-reliance on mental abstraction—maps produced from primary stimuli by the brain—leads to numbness. Lost are the visceral sensations pulsating through the fleshy creature below the mind's ivory tower. We know ourselves more and more by mental maps, by abstract ideas and cognitive concepts of living.

Mechanistic views of breathing dissociate the experience of breathing from its structure and process, thereby reinforcing the mind-body split.

We'll never know who discovered breathwork, pranayama, and other breath-centered practices–just as we'll never know the name of the individual who discovered fire. Of course, there are myths and legends in different cultures and times that say otherwise. For instance, there's Shiva, the Hindu god of yoga, and Hephaestus, Greek god of metallurgy (you may be more familiar with his Roman name, Vulcan). From time immemorial, shamanic traditions have employed breath-centered practices in healing rituals.

Prana

The Sanskrit word *prana*, like the Chinese word *chi* (also spelled *qi*), is commonly translated as *life-force energy*, the subtle, invisible 'food' that nourishes and sustains every living organism. Prana is the *breath within the breath*. The word *pranayama* combines two Sanskrit words, *prana* and *ayama*, which means enhancement, extension, control.

As explained previously, out of all functions controlled by the autonomic nervous system, only breathing can be made conscious and brought under voluntary control. Conscious breathing, whether or not controlled, enhances functioning by the effect it has on the autonomic nervous system. Yogis discovered long ago that breathing a certain way—or simply fixing their attention on it—enhanced the flow of this mysterious energy. They may not have understood anything about oxygen or carbon dioxide. They didn't need to because they were much more interested in results than in explanations.

TWENTY-EIGHT

Inspired Yet?

To become a welcome vessel for the breath is to live life without trying to control, grasp, or push away. And how easy is this? The process of breathing is the most accurate metaphor we have for the way that we personally approach life, how we live our lives, and how we react to the inevitable changes that life brings us.[1]

Donna Farhi

Are you convinced of the power of psychosomatic mind/body medicine yet? The practices you're about to learn will help you perform under stress. Breathwork combined with a positive mindset will enable you to recapture stress energy and use it to build resilience. You'll also recover faster. This alone can make a huge difference because you will no longer be carrying all that excess baggage with you everywhere you go.

The reason yoga, breathwork, and meditation–breath-centered

practices–are called mind/body practices is that they heal the mind-body split. As one of my students put it,

> *I don't come to learn new tricks or fancy postures. I come to knit all the parts and pieces back together.*

Kyle

Even the simple act of observing your own breathing, which is the basis of many meditation techniques, bridges the mind-body split. It is an excellent technique you can practice between tasks throughout your day to lower stress.

At the other extreme, transformational breathwork can be a life-changing experience. Either one-on-one or in a group, you are led by a trained breath-worker through the process of reliving old traumas as a way to release them, thereby freeing you from their harmful influence on your life.

Breath training will help you perform under stress. Breath training is for everyone, whether the crisis should be a matter of life and death or a matter of surviving the cumulative effects of a daily commute. You don't have to be on the front lines—you needn't be a soldier or police officer—to suffer the ill effects of stress. But if breath training can help the policeman, it certainly will help you.

Beyond the direct benefits of health and vitality, energy and mood, concentration and self-mastery, these skills transfer to other arenas of life, such as relationships and work. Take it from Tony Briggs, a veteran Iyengar yoga teacher who admits to an initial resistance to breath work:

> Despite my original dislike of Pranayama, I can testify that it's worth your effort. After a while, I began to notice that

during the 15 or 20 minutes I was practicing, I felt calmer, quieter, more centered, more in touch with the pulses of my breath, body, and mind. The change wasn't dramatic, but over time, I became more familiar with those qualities—and not just on the micro level of my [actual] practice, but on the macro level of my whole life.[2]

Tony Briggs

The Inner Gyroscope

Stillness is like a perfectly centered top, spinning so fast it appears motionless. It appears this way not because it isn't moving, but because it's spinning at full speed. Stillness is not the absence or negation of energy, life, or movement. Stillness is dynamic. It is un-conflicted movement, life in harmony with itself, skill in action. It can be experienced whenever there is total, uninhibited, un-conflicted participation in the moment you are in — when you are wholeheartedly present with whatever you are doing.[3]

Erich Schiffman

If you have ever played with a spinning top, marveled at the awe-inspiring power of a hurricane or tornado, or wondered what keeps a jet plane level and upright even when passing through major atmospheric turbulence, then you have some idea of why having a strong inner center, a good gyroscope in other words, is essential for anyone who wants to thrive, not merely survive.

Gyroscope Inside Hurricane Lantern

The breath-centered practices you're about to learn will strengthen your nervous system, increase your resilience, and prepare you for the internal 'fog and friction' that stress causes. These techniques and practices can improve the quality of your life with their beneficial effects on every aspect of your functioning, through how it affects your energy level, mood state, clarity of thinking, etc. Each one will create immediate results. Practicing them will help you perform better, especially during stressful situations. You will learn to transform stress into productive energy. You'll recover from stress faster. This alone can make a huge difference because you will no longer be carrying all that excess baggage with you everywhere you go.

Beyond Resilience

My goal is to help people like you—people who are basically healthy, well adjusted, and successful. Breath-centered practices cultivate the balance, resilience, and focus you need to perform at your best and reach your full potential.

In a nutshell, you will decide to try breath-centered practices for one of two reasons: you think it might solve a pressing problem (stress, insomnia, anxiety, depression, etc.) or because you imagine they will be enjoyable to do. Either reason is perfectly valid because even if solving an immediate need is what gets you started with breath-centered practices, you will eventually arrive at the second reason—joy. Enjoying life right here, right now, one half-breath at a time is every person's ultimate goal. Right? Beyond health, well-being, and resilience, happiness is what breath-centered practices are ultimately about.

Breath-centered practices cultivate resilience, and with greater resilience comes greater resistance to stress and disease. It is that simple. I want you to understand the critical role fortitude, which includes resilience, plays in your health, in your well-being, as well as in your vitality, success, and happiness.

Breath-centered practices will do more than make you healthier and more resilient. That's just the beginning. But without health, you cannot achieve the other benefits. And if you, like so many of my students, are reading this and are wondering whether the techniques and practices I can teach you will help you with a current health problem, then you're not interested in all those other benefits. Not yet, at least.

My aspiration is that you will be so convinced of the value of the Breath-centered Practices presented in parts 4 and 5 that you will invest the modest amount of time and energy necessary to learn them. Finally—and this is the only thing that will give you the results you want—you will become committed to incorporating breath-centered practices into your daily life— into your own unique, custom tailored version of the Breath-Centered Lifestyle. I cannot wait to share that joy!

Breath-Centered Practices

Pranayama is at once a physical-health practice, mental-health practice, and meditation. It is not just breath training; it's mind training that uses the breath as a vehicle. Pranayama makes your entire life better.[4]

Within the yoga tradition of pranayama alone there are a million different techniques. I've tried 'em all. Every single one. Not! One reason breath-centered practices include techniques for mind, body, heart, and spirit stems from the fact that Kundalini Yoga, as taught by Yogi Bhajan, was my first yoga.

Spectrum of Modalities and Practices

From stress reduction to extraordinary states of consciousness, from garden-variety anxiety to post-traumatic stress disorder— and everything in between—there's a technique that involves some form of breathwork.

Question: Are breath-centered practices the same thing as breathwork?

Have you ever found yourself on one of Wikipedia's disambiguation pages? It's where the word you're searching for means different things in different fields. Well, I got them disambiguation blues again. I need to clarify the difference between breathwork and breath-centered practices in case I have not done so already. They're the same, mostly. They're also different because breath-centered practices, as I define them, include techniques and practices not typically thought of as breathwork.

The following list, despite being incomplete, shows the diversity within the fields encompassed by breath-centered practices:

Breath-oriented

- Pranayama
- Coherent Breathing™
- Transformational Breathwork
- Holotropic Breathwork
- Rebirthing
- Integrative Breathing
- Therapeutic Breathwork
- Buteyko

Body-oriented

- Hatha Yoga (asana practice)
- Five Rhythms
- Tai Chi, Chi Gong
- Breathwalk

Mind-oriented

- Vipassana

- Zen
- Mindfulness-based Stress Reduction
- Yogic Meditation

Heart-oriented

- Inner Balance, Quick Coherence Technique (Heartmath)
- Osho Active Meditations
- Biodynamic Release

TWENTY-NINE

Your Wind Instrument

Think of your body as a musical instrument, a
wind instrument. Your breath, accordingly,
is the wind through the instrument. As
such, it is the single most important aspect
of yoga technique.[1]

Erich Schiffman

I n music, rhythms are created by repeating notes in a
specific order–over and over again. In breathing, rhythm
is composed of breath cycles which repeat continuously
from birth to death. Each breath is a distinct event, meaning it
has a beginning and it has an ending. And it repeats over and
over again, thus creating rhythms. Throughout the body, each
physiological process has its distinctive rhythm: breath cycles,
heartbeat patterns, vascular pulse, brain waves, the peristaltic
contractions of digestion, etc.

The only way you can move from these super-high anxiety

states to calmer more cognitive states, is rhythm [...]
Patterned, repetitive rhythmic activity: walking, running,
dancing, singing, repetitive meditative breathing. You use
brain stem related somatosensory network regulation, which
makes your brain accessible to relational reward and cortical
thinking.[2]

Dr. Bruce Perry

Yehudi Menuhin

Arguably the greatest violinist of his time, Yehudi Menuhin was
also master of another instrument: his body. He studied Hatha
Yoga with B. K. S. Iyengar. Menuhin penned the foreword to
his guru's seminal work, Light on Yoga, which many yoga
teachers and training programs use to settle debates regarding
any and all things yoga; Light on Yoga continues to serve as
their 'yoga bible.'

The way he describes his yoga practice sounds to me like it must
also have been his approach to the daily discipline of practicing
the violin:

> With unflagging patience we refine and animate every cell as
> we return daily to the attack, unlocking and liberating
> capacities otherwise condemned to frustration and death.

I particularly like the fact that he talks about practicing yoga as
performance rather than as practice. Calling it practice implies
that one is never doing the real thing. Menuhin describes his
time on the yoga mat as though it were a live performance.
And, indeed, it is. Every single time. If you're awake.

Menuhin also says something quite profound about the

primacy of our experience of the world 'through the body.' I hear an echo of the adage, *man is the measure of all things,* when he says:

> The practice of Yoga induces a primary sense of measure and proportion. Reduced to our own body, our first instrument, we learn to play it, drawing from it maximum resonance and harmony.

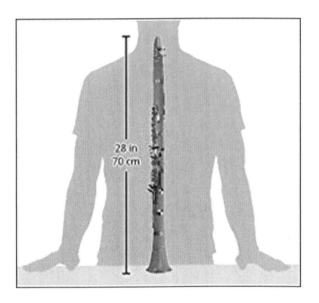

Clarinet & Figure

Menuhin knew a thing or two, to say the least, about the profound relationship between music and breathing:

> Calmness comes with quiet, consistent breathing and the expansion of the lungs. Continuity and a sense of the universal come with the knowledge of the inevitable alternation of tension and relaxation in eternal rhythms of

which each inhalation and exhalation constitutes one cycle, wave or vibration among the countless myriads which are the universe.

More than anything else, I want you to start enjoying breathing a little more. While you're reading this book, and especially as you're doing the exercises and inquiries, allow yourself to simply do what you're doing in the moment. Be present. For that time span, those moments you spend focused on your breathing, indulge yourself in the simple pleasure of rhythm. The simple act of turning one's attention to the cyclical pattern of breathing can be profoundly calming. It takes no more than two or three cycles for a feeling of pleasure to arise, for

> Rhythm is one of the most powerful of pleasures, and when we feel a pleasurable rhythm we hope it will continue. When it does, it grows sweeter. When it becomes reliable, we are in a kind of body-heaven.
>
> -Mary Oliver

Inquiry: Listen to the sound your breath is making for 30 seconds. Listen for the difference in pitch, volume, and timbre between the two. Right now, in terms of its rhythm, is your breathing pattern flowing, staccato, chaotic, or lyrical? Feel free to substitute a more apt descriptor.

Yoga is a state of being as well as an activity; the state of *being yoga* is the state of being the eye of the storm, of being the inner gyroscope that produces skilled action. Being yoga is being that perfectly spinning top. Practice develops the strength, flexibility, and balance which results in equipoise regardless of circumstance. For me, the regular practice of yoga keeps me 'in the zone' more of the time, so that my thoughts, words, and actions are appropriate to the situation. I am more present, more of the time, to the magnificence and the joy of being alive!

THIRTY

Getting Started

Breath-centered practices are free, simple and easy. You can practice them any time, anywhere. You will enjoy many benefits if you follow the instructions and guidelines. However, realizing the benefits depends entirely on you. This book can only lead you to water. You have to drink.

The topic of home practice is often confronting because many of us feel we do not practice enough and we, therefore, feel sheepish when the subject comes up. This is especially true for teachers because we expect ourselves to model the ideal by practicing a minimum of 23 hours every day! Ideally, my practice would always be an exuberant expression of my love and enjoyment of the practice itself. However, this is not always the case. I do practice more days than not; in any given week there may be a day or two when I do not practice. But I rarely go more than two days in a row without practicing. Because, after three days, I notice the difference. I begin to 'lose steam' in all areas of life and overreact to difficulties. I make poor choices; I am not as much fun to be around!

Sometimes, when I am feeling sluggish, my practice serves the purpose of getting me into action; other times, when I am focused or anxious, my practice slows me down and grounds me.

Simply put, the best reason to make breath-centered practices an integral part of your week is that you feel better than when you don't! Once you make breath-centered practices a regular part of your life you will reap ever-increasing benefits. The minimum practice to do is at least twenty minutes three times per week. Any less and the gains of your practice are lost between sessions. The results may not seem dramatic at first. One day, after perhaps three months of regular practice, you will suddenly notice that you feel significantly stronger, more flexible and balanced–physically, emotionally and mentally. You notice being more energetic, more light-hearted, and the time delay between having an intention and manifesting it decreases.

Instant Gratification

I caution you not to approach this as a project–not the way you approach your other projects at least. Lifestyle habits don't work like that. There is a fundamental difference in how you should approach establishing your personal practice and how you approach a project at work. Say you're working towards a deadline, one of those Friday close-of-business-day deadlines. You're responsible for a major project. Your actions must be linear and sequential. There can be only one moment you can celebrate, and that, of course, is when the project is 100% complete. You postpone anything and everything you can. You skip lunch and work extra hours. In short, you delay gratification.

Instead of delaying gratification until the entire goal has been accomplished you design it into the habit itself. Instead of doing without and relying instead on motivation, willpower, and self-discipline, you reward yourself immediately. Every time you do the breath technique you reward yourself again. You'll want to do your new practice not because it's a step closer to your aspiration but because of the instant payoff, the celebration. The more you do it, the greater the pleasure. Soon you'll forget all about getting to your desired future. You'll no longer be pursuing happiness because you're living it.

Prudent Precautions

Many of us are walking around completely unaware of what's really going on in our bodies, in our somatic 'holding-tank,' where all those experiences and emotions we want to ignore are stored. Bringing our attention into this space, into the body, via the bridge of breathwork, can awaken a lot of repressed material. The historical literature of yoga specifically warns against experimenting intemperately with breathing exercises; this often-quoted verse from the *Hatha Yoga Pradipika* is typical:

> Just as lions, elephants, and tigers are gradually controlled, so the prana is controlled through practice. Otherwise the practitioner is destroyed. [1]

Trauma-Sensitive Mindfulness

Back in 1979 when I first experienced the transformative power of the breath in Kundalini Yoga, there was no such thing as trauma-sensitive yoga, mindfulness, or meditation. The only people doing yoga back in those days were seekers, individuals looking for ways to grow spiritually and manifest their full potential. But ever since Rodney Yee made his first appearance on The Oprah Show in 1999, more and more people have taken to yoga and meditation–for reasons other than spiritual development.

Yoga pranayama and other forms of breathwork have taken longer to emerge into mainstream culture, but it looks like its time has arrived. And just like yoga and meditation, breathwork can do more harm than good if practiced inappropriately.

> Though anyone can experience a negative effect of meditation, trauma survivors can be particularly susceptible. The first reason is that trauma survivors usually avoid distressing memories or feelings associated with the trauma— and meditation often involves leaning toward our internal experiences, which includes difficult thoughts and sensations.
>
> The second reason is that trauma may prompt feelings of shame *that can make it difficult to access self-compassion...*
>
> Sometimes in meditation, it is the first time someone is asked to direct loving feelings toward themselves. This can be a very difficult thing to do, and it can result in feeling emotionally overwhelmed.[2]

This kind of leaning in toward difficult emotions can prompt tough stuff to come up for anyone, not just trauma survivors, says Britton. Adding to the complexity is that it's difficult to predict who might experience a negative response. Britton's study identified more than 50 types of negative experiences, which means the vast array and scope of what can come up can make it hard for teachers and practitioners to know what's normal, as well as when someone may need additional support during or after meditating."[3]

Sometimes it can cause moments of discomfort when we start doing these practices. Yes, I'm saying it: it's not always peace and bliss from the get-go. But this buried pain will do you more damage in the long run if it remains in the dark.

If you have a history of trauma or mental illness (anxiety?), it may be wise to consult with your therapist before you begin these practices. Initially, you may find yourself face-to-face with stored feelings & memories. While this is an important step in the healing journey, it may be difficult or disturbing at first. However, many mental health professionals recognize that this process is vital for coming to terms with those traumatic experiences, and achieving peace.

THIRTY-ONE

The Gardener In The Garden

Only he who sees all as self sees correctly.[1]

Rig Veda

I sometimes jokingly refer to Yoga as a Trojan horse: if you seriously practice the techniques for long enough, its ultimate lesson will eventually dawn within you. All the treasured notions of being a separate, autonomous individual shatter and fall away, revealing the eternal and infinite essence of this Universe as your very own essence. It may sound trite, but the fact is, as the Grateful Dead put it in their song of the same name, *You are the eyes of the world.* Pure subjectivity–the center of you, your "I," is the center of the universe. And the center is everywhere!

All Life is Yoga

Nature, the Universe, Existence has evolved life over millions and billions of years, unconsciously. In fact, Sri Aurobindo calls the process of evolution Nature's *unconscious Yoga.*[2]

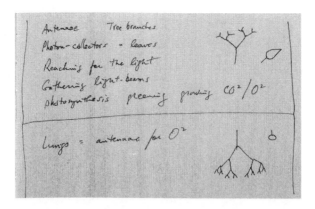

Bronchial tree system mirrors tree root system
(drawing from author's journal)

Conscious Yoga, on the other hand, is whatever you–as an individual human part of the whole of Nature and it's unconscious Yoga–do to work with or improve what Nature has evolved. Yoga is anything you do to cultivate health, prosperity, abundance, happiness, and fulfillment. Yoga is anything you do to reach your full potential. Anything that helps is Yoga.

Yoga is nothing more or less than the conscious adaptation and application of Nature's unconscious process of evolution; Yoga is a means, a technology, by which the individual human can accelerate the natural process of evolution. Yoga operates on the same basic principles as evolution and has been an integral part of the evolution and development of human capacity since prehistory. This concern with the development of human potential is global and has been called by many names other than Yoga, such as shamanism, medicine man, mensch, wise woman, human potential movement.[3]

ALL LIFE IS YOGA (Sri Aurobindo
commemorative coin)

By this definition, you began practicing Yoga when you first, as a child, consciously decided to learn and to change. Yoga is what you do whenever you choose to eat more healthy food, get more sleep, exercise more, work on your relationships, go back to school, plan for your retirement, go on a vacation, or simply do something just for the fun of it!

Yoga—including physical (*asana*), breathing (*pranayama*), and meditation (*dhyana*) practices—is anything and everything one does to enhance life, to sustain, maintain, or optimize the body, heart, mind, and spirit one has been gifted by Nature at birth.

Espalier: Enhancing the Beauty of Nature's Unconscious Yoga

Breath-centered practices, by this definition, are techniques, practices, and activities by which you enhance, extend, magnify, cooperate with, or improve upon nature. Like a gardener, you cultivate your garden and help it grow.

Axel Erlandson with espaliered tree

As American as apple pie, breath-centered practices serve life, liberty, and the joy of the pursuit of happiness.

One World United By Breathing

Yoga—and by extension, breath-centered practices—carries within its practices a specific worldview that may be different from the colored spectacles—all received notions, myths, and other forms of cultural conditioning—through which you perceive and interpret experience. This difference shows up most clearly in the respectively received notions each transmits as to of what an individual is, and of what the relationship should be between individualism and collectivism.

Breathing unites the inside of your body with the entire atmosphere. When you breathe in oxygen, you are inhaling the 'exhale' of plants; when you exhale, you provide the carbon dioxide required by plants to create more oxygen.

The separateness of ego is a natural, emergent outgrowth of the immune system. The immune system's basic task is to distinguish self from not-self, friend from foe, nutritious external food from poisonous, harmful food or bacteria or virus. The ego works exactly the same way albeit in the realm of human interaction. If your immune system and your ego were not functioning in this way to keep your 'castle' safe and healthy then you would not be capable of reading or understanding this right now!

Breath-centered practices bridge the nonmaterial, intangible, metaphysical dimension–what Dr. Dan Siegel calls the *mindsphere*[4], with the material, tangible, physical world of matter.

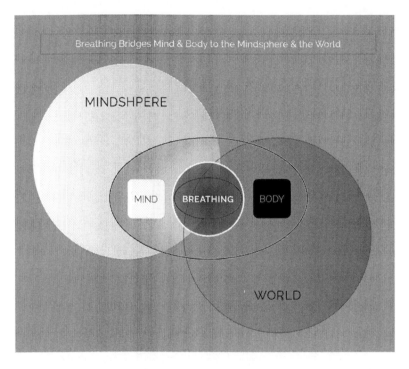

Breath Bridges Mind and Body With Both Immaterial
Consciousness and the Material World

The Fruits Of Practice

Breath-centered practices can improve the quality of your life with their beneficial effects on every aspect of your functioning through how it affects your energy level, mood state, clarity of thinking, etc. Each one will create immediate results. Practicing them will help you perform better, especially during stressful situations. You will learn to transform stress into productive energy. You'll recover from stress faster. This alone can make a huge difference because you will no longer be carrying all that excess baggage with you everywhere you go. Breath-centered practices bring you home, back to the place you've been too busy to visit—your living, breathing body.

From there, the sky's the limit: they can take you to Heaven, into altered states of consciousness as high as the stars (as I was after one breath intensive in India). I call it my mountaintop experience. I can only describe it with paltry words: bliss, the Garden of Eden, the peace that surpasses understanding.

THIRTY-TWO

Begin

_____

Spend a little less time attending to your thoughts today. Spend a little more time today breathing consciously. Do this now. Do this whenever it occurs to you–and it will occur to you.[1]

Erich Sciffman

W hile you may not be able to establish and sustain a dedicated daily practice right away, that's not a problem with breath-centered practices. Let me say it again: breath-centered practices begins the moment you pay conscious attention to breathing and sustain it, one breath at a time. It's really as simple as that.

On the other hand, if you do establish the habit of conscious breathing, if you do make these practices a habit, then you will be rewarded with dividends far greater than your investment. The rewards grow, accrue, and soon snowball by the power of compound interest.

Are you convinced by what you've read so far? Ready to try what I have in store for you?

What are you waiting for? Just begin as you intend to continue, one half-breath after another...

Practice Selector

- **Your First Breath Practice** (location: Introduction)
- **Quick Scan** (location: multiple)
- **When Do I Hold My Breath? 1** (location: Part 1, Distress Call)
- **Drop It! Technique** (location: Part 1, Buddha's Four Noble Truths)
- **When Do I Hold My Breath? 2** (location: Part 1, Disease)
- **How many breaths do I breathe per minute?** (location: Part 2, Curing Hypertension)
- **When Do I Hold My Breath? 3** (location: Part 2, True Pudding)
- **When Do I Hold My Breath? 4** (location: Part 2, Veterans With PTSD)

- **Gratitude, One Half-Breath At A Time** (location: Part 3, A Most Common Miracle)
- **Locate (Befriend) Your Diaphragm** (location: Part 4, Introduction to Breath-centered Practices)
- **Tiny Habits** Install one or more new breathing habits into your daily routine. (location: Part 6, Design Your Habit)

Featured Practices (location: Part 5: Instructions)

- **Breath Inquiry:** Befriend breathing; observe and assess your breathing habits; activate the relaxation response.
- **Easy Yoga For Breath:** Increase the flexibility and strength of the breathing system.
- **Diaphragmatic Breathing:** Develop optimal, complete breath.
- **Coherent Breathing™:** Develop slow, effortless rhythm and establish resonance with heart rhythm (increase HRV).
- **Synchronized Walking:** Synchronize body, breath, and heart rhythms.
- **Joy For Joy's Sake:** Gratitude Breathing
- **Centering The Storm (Fifty-To-Zen):** Cultivate mindfulness, experience thoughtless state (awareness independent of thinking).
- **Tiny Habits:** Install one or more new breathing habits into your daily routine. Part 6, Design Your Habit

INSTRUCTIONS

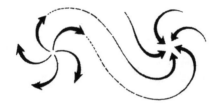

THIRTY-THREE

Breath Inquiry

The Breath Inquiry is the point of embarkation on your private expeditionary journey that is breathwork. I recommend making it a special occasion; I also heartily recommend you write about your experience. Write down your answers to the questions provided; they establish a baseline for next time. Start a dedicated breathwork journal; it will enrich your experience, hone your powers of observation, reveal your unique patterns of not only breathing but also of being. Keeping a breathwork journal will empower and accelerate your progress.

Whether you practice the Breath Inquiry once or a hundred times, you can never exhaust its potential for self-revelation. Just as you cannot step into the same river twice, you cannot repeat the same Breath Inquiry. At first, breathing may seem vague and without discernible features, like white noise or fog. This exercise will develop your ability to appreciate its rich tapestry. Any time you start out to improve a thing or a behavior, you must first observe and measure it. Prior to studying anatomy and physiology, before learning how to breathe optimally, you need to know what you're working with. Investigate your body as it breathes. Be curious. Forget what you think you know. Look afresh. Reject all mental images and memories, all second-hand, indirect knowledge. Allow yourself to be a beginner, even if you have done this before.

The objective and subjective domains of breathing are mutually exclusive. What we typically talk about when we talk about breathing are its physical aspects: ventilation, respiration, and the cardiorespiratory functional unit. In short, the anatomy and physiology of breathing. In contradistinction to these body processes, inquiry is a subjective process, in the sense of being your private experience.

This may sound complicated and convoluted, but all I am trying to get at here is that the only thing you can ever know, when you boil it down, is your private, subjective experience. Moment by moment, the brain creates images, thoughts, sounds, smells, and other sensations to represent the data delivered to it by the afferent nerves. When you get right down to it, there's no essential difference—in actual experience—between inside and outside.

I'll say to you what I say to my students: I bet you know more about the inside of your refrigerator than you do about the inside of your own body! Give yourself ample time for this meet-and-greet; get reacquainted with your long-lost companion, your estranged partner. Don't take my word for it, nor anyone else's. This is your breathing.

And what is the best way to learn about it? Go straight to the source. Conduct your own investigation. Do you know the original meaning of the word autopsy? Look with your own eyes! Know thyself! No one besides you can ever know your experience of breathing. Have faith in your own observations, and trust the authority of your own experience.

Benefits

You cannot control something you cannot measure. Before you can measure breath, you have to observe it. Before attempting to control your breathing, you need to observe it, feel it, experience it, and measure it. Later on you'll learn how to modify and control your breathing in specific ways, but for now, during the breath inquiry, you're not to change or control or manage breathing whatsoever.

- Befriend your own body, breath, and mind
- Distinguish first-order, direct perception from second-hand knowledge
- Establish a baseline for future reference
- Begin to develop the distinctions and vocabulary of breathwork:
- Time measures (breath rate, or br/min)
- Volume measures (shallow vs deep)
- Rhythm (flowing, staccato, chaotic, lyrical, quiescent)
- Texture (silky, ragged, dense)
- Discover your personal breathing 'signature'

Time, Set and Setting

Set a time when you will be rested, when you will not fall asleep. Reduce or remove all distractions. Make sure the room is comfortable—not cold, but also not so warm that you'll doze off.

Eliminate every source of distraction or disturbance you possibly can; choose a time and a place that affords the best chance you will not be interrupted. Choose a time when you are neither tired nor wired, when you are relaxed but not in need of sleep. Otherwise, you will fall asleep or be distracted. Choose a place that is quiet, comfortable, and pleasant.

How Long to Practice: minimum five minutes.

Posture & Props

Cover yourself to stay warm if need be. Cover your eyes and ears with an elastic bandage, a sleep mask, or simply close them. Use noise-canceling headphones if possible.

What to Look For (Breath Inquiry)

Be curious! Take a moment to familiarize yourself with the list of questions below before you start. Print them out if you like for easy reference during the practice. Better yet, download the Guided Breath Inquiry and simply follow my instructions.

- Is my breathing shallow or deep?
- Fast or slow?
- Which is longer: inhale or exhale?
- Which moves more: belly, low ribs, or top chest?
- Where does my inhale originate?
- Where does my exhale disappear to?
- What image or word best describes my breath pattern- flowing, staccato, chaotic, lyrical, or subtle? What image best describes the quality of my breathing- wave-like, billowy, strained, robust, inhibited, lethargic, streaming, powerful, molasses, erratic, or steady?
- How many breaths do I breathe per minute? The last part of this exercise determines your rate of breathing by counting how many breaths you take per minute. You will count each exhale for two minutes and then

divide that number in half to arrive at an average. What is my breathing rate?

Practice Instructions

And now, step by step:

1. Settle in for a few moments. Gradually guide your attention to focus on the real-time experience of breathing. Do NOT change or improve or control your breathing in any way. Just observe!
2. Relax and observe your own breathing. And remember not to control it or change it in any way, if possible. Be curious!
3. If you use the Breath Inquiry audio[1]: Once you are settled into a comfortable position (seated or lying down), click the Next button and close your eyes. Allow your attention to be guided as you explore your breathing. At the end, a chime will indicate the end of the inquiry.
4. When you are finished, open your eyes and stretch.

Follow-Up questions for reflection

- Was it easy to concentrate on exclusively breathing?
- If not, why? What interfered? Worries, concerns, anxiety, memories, plans?
- How do I feel after practicing the breath inquiry? Relaxed? Agitated?
- Compare your pulse and blood pressure before and after with a BP cuff device.
- Compare breaths per minute before and after. Better

yet, have a friend do it for you since merely observing
it changes your breathing!

- Pair up with another person. Take turns being observer
  and observed.
- Repeat the "When Do I Hold My Breath?' inquiries
  (or repeat them, if you skipped the separate inquiries
  sprinkled throughout the book)
- Write down what you learned about yourself.
- How many breaths did you take in two minutes?
- Is pure observation a calming practice for you?

To use the free audio guided practice, visit
josephroberson.com/resources.

THIRTY-FOUR

Easy Yoga For Breath

Practice this short, easy, and simple yoga sequence as preparation for breathwork, for meditation, to feel better–or just for the pleasure of doing it! It does not take much time to do. This sequence tunes every part of your 'wind instrument,' from your toes to the crown of your head, with emphasis on those that directly affect breathing: spine, core muscles, diaphragm, chest, and shoulders.

It does not take much time to do this simple and easy yoga routine. While a daily practice is best, the minimum frequency is at least every third day.

To prevent the accumulation of the effects of stress, never allow more than two days between sessions. It works just like compound interest!

Benefits

- Stretches and strengthens the muscles of breathing
- Reduces stiffness, particularly in the rib cage and spine

- Fosters correct posture, which alone can dramatically improve breathing by freeing up the diaphragm
- Removes the physical effects of momentary stress and prevents those effects from becoming a permanent part of the body's somatic memory
- Stimulates the lymphatic system to increase elimination of waste products from the cells and organs

Time, Set and Setting

You can complete this sequence in less than 10 minutes. You can also extend it however long you like simply by repeating each exercise. If you have just a few additional minutes, however, I encourage you to do the optional meditation at the end—it only adds an additional 7-10 minutes. Eliminate all environmental distractions so you will not be disturbed or distracted during the exercise.

Posture & Props

Sit comfortably but with good posture, spine erect without slumping.

Practice Sequence

1. Foot Massage

Foot Massage

Start with right foot crossed over left leg, weave left fingers in between toes of right foot:

1. Fingers between toes, rotate ankle. Then twist and pull each toe individually. Bend all five toes down to stretch the top of your foot.
2. Change hands, bend all five toes up to stretch the long plantar tendon, which runs along the inner edge of the bottom of your foot. If it pops up and feels like a steel cable, it is shortened and needs regular massaging to stretch it out. Otherwise, it can cause plantar fasciitis!
3. Next, massage the whole foot with both hands in any way that feels good! Pay extra attention to the ball of your foot as well as any place that feels tight.
4. To stimulate and increase blood flow, use both hands to 'pink' your foot. In other words, clap your hands with your foot in between. For this to work it must sting a little. So, clap loudly!
5. Finally, give this foot a gentle shake to release any last remaining tightness, particularly in the ankle.

Repeat with your other foot.

2. Row Boat

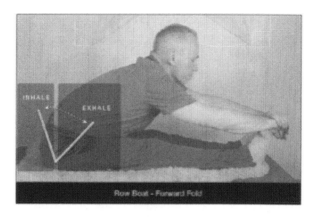

Row Boat

1. Sit with your legs close together and extended out straight. As best you can, keep both your legs and your trunk straight as you do the movement. If your hamstrings are tight, bend your knees rather than your back.

2. Extend both arms and point them straight forward above your knees. Keep your arms horizontal, level with the floor; this is not about touching your toes! If you attempt to touch your toes, then your back will almost certainly round. If your body is extremely stiff you have no choice, but the idea is to isolate the movement to the forward and backward tilting of your hips. That's the action that stretches the hamstrings.

3. The pelvis moves the same way in Pelvic Rock (below).

4. Sit with your back against a wall to do the rowboat. Initiate the forward tilt from the back of your pelvis, from the top of your sacrum. If you've ever seen one of those "Dippy Bird" toys you can picture yourself moving as it does—by hinging forward and back from your hip sockets.

5. Move slowly. Honor your limitations. Above all, never

'bounce' or apply force. In case you don't know, tendons and ligaments take a long time to heal. Much longer than muscle. If you overdo it, you'll have to nurse your hamstrings back to health. And lose any progress made. As my teacher wisely put it, the slow way is the fast way. Nowhere is this truer than with stretching.

6. As you exhale, hinge forward from your hip sockets. Keep your arms up as if you are reaching to touch the opposite wall, not your toes.

7. As you inhale, reverse; rock back to the starting position—or just a little beyond vertical. There is no benefit in rocking way back.

8. Repeat this rowing movement slowly and gently for one to three minutes.

9. To finish, exhale forward and stay for one to three minutes in a seated forward fold (Paschimottanasana in Sanskrit). Fold over your outstretched legs—without rounding your back or bending your knees. For at least three breaths, intensify the stretch. Lengthen your spine toward your toes as far as you can, but not so far that the sensations shift to pain. The guiding principle, here and always, is to nudge past your own limit. But never to cause harm. What's the easiest way to know when to stop pushing? When your breathing stops or becomes ragged.

10. After a few seconds, when you've encountered your edge, where the sensations are as intense as you desire, go ahead and relax. Back off a little. Allow your back to round now.

11. Soften enough that your breath flows and all discomfort fades. Remain like this long enough for the stretch to soak through. While you're here, gently move your head around. Loosen your neck. Stretch

your mouth open. Scrunch up your face and then release all the facial muscles. Pretend you're erasing the tension lines from your face, the way you erase the lines of a drawing from an Etch-a-Sketch toy.

3. The Grind

Sit with legs crossed, hands on knees.

Press both sitting bones, also called the *sitz bones*[1], down to lengthen spine up as if your crown is rising up to touch the sky.

Rotate your pelvis, like a tilted water bucket, from one sitting bone to your tailbone. Continue, rotating your pelvis in the same direction, from your tailbone around to the opposite sitting bone. Continue around to the front, and back again to the first sitting bone. You should feel how each hip socket rotates over the ball-shaped end (head) of the thigh bone (femur), like a ball-and-socket joint. You are rotating the socket, not the ball.

After 5-10 revolutions, repeat in the opposite direction.

4. Pelvic Rock

Still sitting cross-legged, press down with your sitz bones. Pressing downward through the sitz bones enlists the deep core muscles to create a natural lengthening all the way up through the neck and head. This little trick is an easy way to establish (or reestablish) the four natural curves of anatomical neutral.

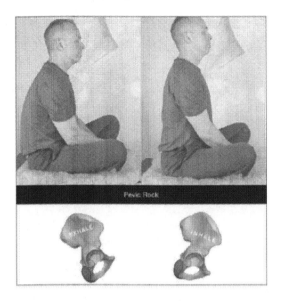

Pelvic Rock

Exhale as you rock backward, tilting your pelvis backward onto the tailbone. Inhale and rock forward, tilting the pelvis forward on your sitz bones ('rockers').

Be mindful not to jut your chin forward; keep your chin level and horizontal so the back of your neck is long.

Hold the shins just above the ankles. Move from lower back and sacrum.

On an exhale, use your abs to squeeze more air out to complete the exhale, on the inhale press sit bones to lengthen your spine. End by inhaling deeply, hold breath briefly before exhaling (3x).

5. Side Bend (Lateral Spine Stretch)

Sit with legs crossed, right hand on floor beside right hip. Press sitz bones down to lengthen up with a tall spine, engage core muscles to prevent lower spine from bending. Reach left arm overhead and curve torso over to the right from your heart, emphasizing the thoracic/middle spine (opening side ribs).

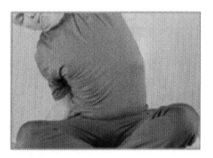

Side Bend (Lateral Spine Stretch)

Once you get the basic movement, alternate left and right sides with your breath: inhale first then exhale and bend to the right. As you inhale, sit up straight, back to square one. As you exhale, bend over the left side. Inhale straight. Repeat at least six times on each side.

6. Shoulder Circles

Remain seated in a cross-legged position. Hands resting on knees, rotate your shoulders up, back, and down several times, ending with shoulder blades firmly engaged to back ribs 'like refrigerator magnets.' Always rotate your shoulders back, never forward (to counter the habit of hunching forward).

7. Middle Spine Flex

Sit up tall and grasp the underside of the (outer) knees. Circle your shoulders up toward your ears, then back from your ears, and finally downward as you pull your inner shoulder blades a little closer together.

Each time you exhale, round your back; imagine your sternum passing-between your shoulders as you curl as though into a ball. This stretches the back side of the rib cage and creates more space between those ribs.

Each time you inhale, pull your heart (breastbone, or sternum) forward of your shoulders. This action flexes the thoracic segment of your spine like a backbend.

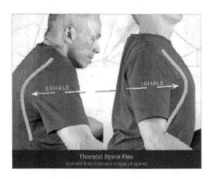

Middle Spine Flex

8. Washing Machine

Hands on shoulders, fingers in front, thumbs on back.

Engage your core by toning the lower abdomen in. Press both sitz bones down to lengthen spine up as if your crown is rising up to touch the sky.

Washing Machine Twist

Keeping the sitz bones firmly grounded, inhale and twist your torso to the right, exhale and twist to the left. Although I learned to do this at a rapid pace in Kundalini Yoga, I recommend a slow pace for beginners. Use your own discretion. Be sure to move from your sternum while keeping your sacrum, sitz bones, pelvis—everything below the navel—stable and do not allow the sitz bones to shift. Keep your chin and head turning in lock-step with the sternum. If the twisting makes you dizzy or nauseous, then you can keep your head straight.

Repeat several times until your spine has warmed up.

Now hold the twist to the right for at least three breaths.

Repeat on the other side: twist left and stay for at least three breaths.

Conclude by inhaling with a tall spine, return to the front and exhale. Relax.

9. Neck & Head

Establish a neutral head position: With your hands resting on your knees, gently rock your head from chin up to chin down until the back of your neck is tall and chin is level.

Engage your core muscles; gently press down into your seat with your sitz bones to establish a firm anchor. Thus grounded, float up from this base and grow subtly taller—as though by an invisible force rebounding from your downward press. Imagine you are lengthening upward from your base all the way up to the top of your head.

10. Easy Seated Pose (Sukhasana)

Align from sitz bones up through crown in 'Seated Mountain.' Now that you have completed the joint-freeing series, this is the ideal moment to pause in a firm, neutral, upright seated posture. Repeat from before:

Engage your core muscles; gently press down into your seat with your sitz bones to establish a firm anchor. Thus grounded, float up from this base and grow subtly taller—as though an invisible force were rebounding from your downward press. Imagine you are lengthening upward from your base all the way up to the top of your head.

11. Stillness

Now, seated in Sukhasana, turn your attention to your breath. Allow it to flow naturally. Enjoy this state of poise, balance, and tranquility. Pause. Linger here for at least a few breaths. Better yet, a few minutes.

12. Optional: Fifty-2-Zen

If you have five more minutes, now is the perfect time to practice the Fifty-2-Zen breath countdown exercise. Refer to that chapter for instructions.

To use the free audio guided practice, visit josephroberson.com/resources.

THIRTY-FIVE

Diaphragmatic Breathing

I f, in the course of doing the Breath Inquiry, you uncovered any suboptimal, disordered breathing habits, this section on Diaphragmatic Breathing will show you how to correct them. All you need to do is follow the step-by-step instructions provided to develop your personal, optimal breath. You will learn how to breathe in the way the system is designed to work, as opposed to breathing partially, haphazardly, or incorrectly.

My students often tell me they are shocked by how much more air they breathe in and out with Diaphragmatic Breathing. Many also describe a sort of rush, or surge, of energy, followed by "Okay, I'm sold! I want to do this every day!"

All you need do is follow the step-by-step instructions provided to realize its benefits. It's well worth the small investment of time it takes, don't you think?

Benefits

- Lowers blood pressure
- Reduces stress on heart muscle by assisting its pumping action
- Increases maximum tidal volume you are capable of, as well as maximum duration of a single breath cycle
- Increases average tidal volume when you are not conscious of breathing, as well as average duration of each breath cycle (breaths per minute)
- Teaches you to breathe the way the respiratory system is designed to work

Time, Set and Setting

Learning Diaphragmatic Breathing takes more time than other techniques. Therefore allow at least 30 minutes. Keep in mind that mastering Diaphragmatic Breathing establishes a solid foundation for every other kind of breathing, including normal, automatic breathing. Invest ample time to master Diaphragmatic Breathing; you will be rewarded with its many benefits each and every day.

In the beginning, set aside 30 minutes or more to learn how to practice correctly. And even after you've mastered Diaphragmatic Breathing, it's essential to do what I call a set-aside practice regularly in order to build this new habit of optimal breathing. Only through a regular practice (no less than once every three days) will you be able to establish a new normal, a new baseline of breathing. Remember, it works by the miracle of compound interest: invest a small amount of time and effort consistently and the benefits grow exponentially over time.

Practice at home or some other quiet room until you learn the technique by heart—until you can do it without thinking much about it. Then employ it in the daily hustle and bustle of life. One of the beauties of Diaphragmatic Breathing is you can practice it just about anywhere and any time. This makes it an ideal 'secret weapon' against stress. No one need know you are practicing it!

Speaking of room, an over-full stomach prevents free movement of the diaphragm, so allow at least an hour after eating before practicing.

Posture and Props

You will be able to concentrate more on learning the intricacies of Diaphragmatic Breathing when lying on your back, in a supine position. No props are required. On the other hand, use any and all means at hand to reduce distraction and increase comfort. Placing a pillow under your knees often makes for a happier low back. Refer to the Breath Inquiry instructions for suggestions on additional props, such as an eye covering.

Keep in mind that you are cultivating the normal and natural state of balance in each and every part and system of your body, breath, heart, and mind. Therefore, sit or stand in such a way that your spine is straight, not slumped. Adjust your posture so your diaphragm has an easy time moving up and down as you inhale and exhale.

After gaining competency in Diaphragmatic Breathing, I recommend practicing in a seated position for comparison. Orientation and posture make a difference. Regardless of your choice, adjust your position until your spine assumes its natural curvature and alignment; any distortion can inhibit the diaphragm's movements.

A comfortable seated position, such as Sukhasana or Siddhasana, works well. Sitting in a chair also works fine—just remember not to slump. Make sure to keep your spine in a tall and aligned position—neither slumped nor rigid. There are two main reasons for this: alertness and room for your diaphragm to move.

If you choose to sit, elevate yourself with a folded blanket or cushion to keep your hips and knees happy. Your knees should be no higher than your navel.

Practice Sequence

1. Check-In (Quick Breath Inquiry)

It's a good habit to begin each session with what I call the Breath Inquiry. You can think of it as a check-in. Call it whatever you like. What counts is to observe your breathing—where you're starting from—before changing it.

Notice everything. Observe your breathing in context, how it reveals not only the physical movements of breathing itself, but also other bodily sensations, feelings, thoughts, and emotions. Think of this as reading the water, as sailors do before setting course. For instance, did you eat too much and have only now become aware of the way an overly full stomach gets in the way of breathing deeply?

Most of all, organize yourself so you are actually ready to pay full attention to the practice, then gradually narrow your attention to just your breathing. Relax and feel the sensations of air as it brushes along the inner nostrils.

2. Squeeze More Air Out on the Exhale

First, locate your diaphragm (review instructions here.)

Now, move your hands to either side of your navel. Palms are flat and around your belly. Adjust them at the conclusion of an exhale, so your fingers barely meet.

Inhale normally, then exhale. At the end of your normal exhale, squeeze more air out by pulling your belly inward. This causes the diaphragm to dome upward inside your ribs. Instead of the normal 1-2 centimeters of total movement up and down, it's possible for it to move 10 centimeters or more. Repeat 5-10 times.

3. Expand Your Belly on the Inhale

Expand the volume of air by allowing your belly to expand like a balloon with each inhale. The goal is to increase the gap between your fingers so your belly resembles a watermelon. Repeat 5-10 times.

4. Expand Lower Ribs Instead of Belly

Move your hands to the sides, wrap them around your low ribs at their widest point. Feel the skin and bones under your palms and fingers. As you begin to inhale, focus on your hands and low ribs. All you need to do is direct the breath so it pushes your hands outward. Feel your rib cage expanding, instead of your belly. This is what your diaphragm is designed to do!

Repeat as many times as you like. The more, the merrier!

5. Expand Middle Ribs

Move your hands up to your middle ribs under the armpits. Practice increasing how much you can expand in the middle lungs. Repeat several times.

6. Expand Top Ribs

Move your hands up and place them to either side of your

collarbones. Practice increasing how much you can expand in the top-most lungs. Repeat several times.

7. All Together Now!

Use a six-count as you combine the expanded movements of lower, middle, and upper ribs for the complete three-part Diaphragmatic Breathing technique:

1. In-hale ... expand lower ribs
2. Three-four ... expand middle ribs
3. Five-six ... expand upper ribs
4. Ex-hale ... release upper ribs
5. Three-four ... release middle ribs
6. Five-six ... release lowest ribs.

Repeat for at least six breath cycles. Gradually ease the effort to maximize your inhale and exhale until you arrive at a smooth, comfortable, slow and deep rhythm you can easily sustain for an indefinite time.

Tip: Don't take these instructions to mean your belly won't move at all. It will expand and contract, but nowhere near as much as in belly breathing. The mental trick, here and always: focus on what you *do* want to happen, not on what you *don't* want to happen.

8. Well Done! Enjoy!

Pause. Linger here for at least a few breaths—better yet, several minutes. Observe again. What differences do you feel compared to before you practiced? Give yourself a pat on the back for investing in yourself! Know that others will notice the difference in your attitude, energy, and presence. Don't be surprised if they start asking you what you're doing that's new. Most of all, enjoy how you feel!

Follow-Up

In case you judge your 'performance' harshly, keep in mind that breathwork is a long game. Relax. In due time you will find you have mastered the technique. Keep your eye on the ideal but don't allow yourself to be waylaid by self-criticism. Just tracking toward it, keep moving in that direction. Steady as she goes!

THIRTY-SIX

Coherent Breathing Symphony

Think of your time spent practicing Coherent Breathing™ as a mini-vacation, an instant retreat, as cultivating your garden. You are taking charge of your own health, well-being, vitality—your own happiness! One of my long-time students calls Coherent Breathing™ "The dessert of my day." She says, "This is part of why I feel it helps me not binge-eat, which is huge!" She recently passed the 600-day milestone on Coherent Breathing Symphony on Insight Timer[1] for practicing Coherent Breathing Symphony every day!

You can purchase the Coherent Breathing Symphony album (3 tracks) from my website (josephroberson.com), CDbaby, or from Coherence.com.

Benefits

- Causes up to a tenfold improvement in heart-rate variability (HRV)—perhaps the best indicator of a healthy autonomic system balance.

- Strengthens immune system function.
- Amplifies peristaltic movements of digestion.
- Improves the quality of sleep.
- Better focus and attention span—thus productivity.
- Reduces emotional reactivity, which can lead to wiser responses.
- Improves the ability to listen and can increase communication effectiveness.
- Healthier relationships, more intimacy, and even better sex!

Set and Setting

Practice at home or some other quiet place until you learn the technique by heart, until you can do it without the need to think much about it. Then you have it in your back pocket, or on your smartphone, so you can practice it anywhere. This makes it an ideal 'secret weapon' against stress. No one will know you are practicing it!

Posture & Props

Keep in mind that you are cultivating the normal and natural state of balance in each and every part and system of your body, breath, heart, and mind. Therefore, sit or stand in such a way that your spine is tall, not slumped. Adjust your posture so your diaphragm has an easy time moving up and down as your inhale and exhale. Be mindful of maintaining good posture, but don't be obsessive about it to the point of adding unnecessary strain. Be as relaxed as possible without slouching. By the way, the Sanskrit word for this balance of effort and ease is *sukha*.

Time

According to Stephen Elliott and other experts, it takes between eight and 12 minutes of breathing at five breaths per minute to achieve synchronization of breathing pattern and heart rhythm. That said, even three minutes reduces stress. However, when possible practice a minimum of eight minutes and a maximum of 30 minutes.

Practice Tips

Use a simple, pleasant metronome sound or meditation timer, such as tracks 2 or 3 of *Coherent Breathing Symphony* to prompt you when to inhale and when to exhale. Setting up a timer to the appropriate pace reduces your cognitive load (the amount of mental work you need to do) while you practice.

It is normal to have anxiety about time. To avoid it, set a timer to free yourself, so you can focus more completely on your practice. You can also instruct Siri, "Wake me up in 30 minutes." This way you won't need to keep checking to see how much time has passed.

It's a good habit to begin each session with what I call the Breath Inquiry. You can call it a check-in, a body scan, whatever you like. What counts is to see where you're starting from. Start by observing your overall state, including thoughts, feelings, energy level, body sensations. Notice everything. How is your breathing pattern affected by your overall state at this moment?

Keep in mind that the calming, soothing effect of Coherent Breathing™ is far more important than the perfection of technique. Otherwise, you risk adding anxiety instead of releasing it. So don't obsess over getting it right!

For instance, if you cannot comfortably breathe at this pace right away, start at a more comfortable pace and slow down gradually. In due time you will find you have mastered the technique. Keep your eye on the ideal but don't allow yourself to be waylaid by self-criticism. Just track toward it, keep moving in that direction. Steady as she goes!

Imagine the rhythms of your breathing and heartbeat gradually coming into phase, into coherence.

Just know you'll get distracted at some point. More likely, many times. This is normal. Don't fret. What should you do? Simply notice it each time it happens, then gently redirect your attention back to your breath. Don't beat yourself up about it. That would just add more turbulence, more incoherence, more discord, on top of what's already in your system! Instead, be patient. Accept it and let it go. It's all part of the game! Loving yourself is a practice in and of itself. But we'll talk more about that when you learn the Gratitude Breathing practice.

Instructions

Coherent Breathing™ is simple. All you do is breathe in for six seconds and out for six seconds. That's 12 seconds per breath and five breaths per minute. Breathe in for six seconds and out for six seconds. Breathe in and out through your nose if possible. Breathe gently and smoothly. Most of all, breathe rhythmically. Do not strain. Relax!

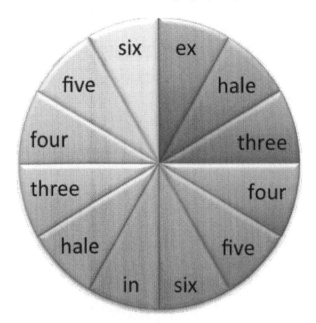

Coherent Breathing practice aid

1. Imagine your breathing as a circle. Imagine your next exhale starting at 12 o'clock and ends at 6 o'clock; the next inhale commences at 6 o'clock and ends at 12 o'clock. Continue like this for at least three minutes.
2. Gently deepen your breath. Without straining, lengthen both your inhale and your exhale. Relax. Breathe gently, smoothly, softly. Even inhale and exhale.
3. Allow your breathing rhythm to become one unbroken circle. In through your nose. Out through relaxed lips.
4. Focus on this half-breath: this inhale, this exhale. One at a time, steady and calm.
5. Continue like this for at least three minutes.

To experience the full effect you have to breathe at this pace for at least 8-12 minutes. That's how long experts say it takes to synchronize your breathing pattern and heart rhythm and generate sympathetic resonance between them.

Visualization of the Inner Gyroscope (optional)

The center of this circle is where you are observing the breath from. This center is the unmoving observer, the witness. The more you practice this simple technique of returning attention first to the breath cycling and then to the act of attention itself, the easier it will become to stay grounded in the facts of what is actually occurring. Less and less time will be lost spinning your wheels in the endless loops of run-on thoughts and habitual, fear-based mood states. You have generated your own inner gyroscope!

When You're Done, Smell the Roses!

Pause. Linger here for at least a few breaths. Better a few minutes. Notice how it feels to be in harmony. Enjoy how coherence feels! Look to your future, your next task, the rest of your breathing days. Smile!

THIRTY-SEVEN

Synchronized Walking

Conscious attention on breathing is (as I have witnessed again and again in my students) the easiest entry to meditation. And combining conscious breathing with walking is the absolute best place to start.

Have you ever found yourself just walking? What I mean is, do you ever have moments when walking is the only thing you're doing? Not thinking about the past. Not thinking about the future. Just walking, just paying attention to what's happening —just doing what you're doing as you're doing it. Sound familiar?

If so, then you've experienced the flow state, also known as absorption, mindfulness, one-pointed concentration and lots of other terms. Meditation!

What works best for me is to practice toward the end of my walk. This way I've already walked off most of the anxious energy and accomplished my exercise goals. In the process, I've already emptied my head to some extent. Thoughts are fewer and further between at least.

Synchronized Walking

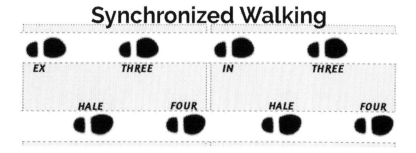

Coherence Walking

I usually start with a four-count and switch to six once I'm comfortable. What matters is the synchronization of walking, breathing, and counting. Not the number.

Benefits

- Simple and easy technique that can be incorporated into daily life
- Encourages walking more and sitting less
- Grounding effect that comes from 'nature bathing,' from immersing yourself in a natural environment
- An easy introduction to the experience of 'whole body breathing'

Time, Set and Setting

Choose a location where you won't need to pay attention to your surroundings. Choose a safe and quiet location, such as a level stretch of sidewalk, park, or nature trail.

Instructions

1. Walk any way you like

As you walk, notice everything. Take an extreme wide-angle view, from one edge of your peripheral vision to the other. This simple trick can be transformative. It breaks the monopoly of tunnel vision.

I usually spend the first 20 minutes walking fast to get a little cardio in before practicing this technique. Maybe you'd like to think of it as a cool-down.

2. Gradually slow down

Toward the end of your walk, down-shift into a slow speed. The image is of a motor or fan slowing because you pulled the plug.

Begin paying less and less attention to what's around you. Focus on what's going on inside. What's the weather like inside? Notice how your breathing reflects your internal state—thoughts, feelings, energy level.

3. Synchronize four steps to each half-breath

Now, it's entirely up to you whether to start on an inhale or an exhale. My personal preference is to always start on an exhale. Just pick one and always start that same way.

1. Ex-Hale-Three-Four
2. In-Hale-Three-Four
3. Ex-Hale-Three-Four
4. In-Hale-Three-Four

That's eight steps during one complete breath cycle: four during exhale and four during inhale.

4. Continue for at least six minutes

You may find it takes a minute or two simply to find your rhythm. What you are looking for is a pace, pattern, and rhythm that feels intuitively right, that you could continue indefinitely. It should eventually feel so easy and right as to seem like the way your breathing and walking are supposed to sync up. Guess what—it is!

5. Return to normal walking (or stop and stand still)

Relax. Notice how much more present you feel. Soak in your surroundings. Hear what you hear. See what you see. Smell what you smell. Be!

THIRTY-EIGHT

Joy For Joy's Sake

Most of us don't need industrial-strength breathwork. That's good news because the practice you're about to learn is geared toward the rest of us. If Power Breath Meditation (Sudarshan Kriya) is strong medicine, then the Gratitude Breath is your daily vitamin. It is most effective as proactive cultivation, but most definitely it is also effective as a therapeutic intervention.

Gratitude Breathing, as with other so-called heart quality cultivation practices, works slowly and gradually. Think of it as cultivating a garden or a relationship: water, but not too much at one time. Easy does it. Like compound interest, the effects accumulate slowly at first but compound and increase exponentially with consistent practice.

Our number-one goal here is emotional health. Emotional health is more important than the breath technique. In other words, you are to focus more on generating the desired heart quality than on doing the breath technique correctly. In heart-centered breathwork practices, breath plays a supporting, rather than leading, role—same as it does in Mindfulness practice.

Don't obsess over the technical details; concentrate your attention more on cultivating the feeling. Tailor your breathing pattern as best supports and augments the feeling.

Benefits

- Joy, for absolutely no reason
- More restful, restorative sleep
- Increases positive affect (light-heartedness, happiness, bliss, contentment)
- Alleviates anxiety, depression, worry (dukkha)

Time, Set and Setting

Practice in a quiet, comfortable place. The light level should be pleasantly low. Eliminate all environmental distractions so you will not be disturbed or distracted during the exercise. Dedicate a 'set aside' time to practice of at least 20 minutes. Do this consistently, at least every third day, preferably every day. Once you have established your chosen heart quality, once it is firmly 'installed,' it will be with you everywhere you go. Practice for a few moments or a few minutes several times a day. Try setting a repeating alert for yourself on your smartphone to remind you. The more often you remember your heart quality and to think, speak, and act from it, the more you become it. At some point, you won't need to practice any longer. You will *be* it!

Posture

Sit comfortably, yet without slumping. Adjust your spine so it is balanced over your sitz bones. Be alert, yet relaxed. Use only as much effort as needed. Create an open-hearted posture, one conducive to generating your chosen quality.

Practice Sequence

1. Scan body, breath, mind, heart

As always, step one is to establish awareness. Pretend you're a ship on the ocean. Drop your anchor right here. Let your anchor down, down below the surface with its waves. Let your anchor plummet down past the undercurrents, all the way home to the solid floor below.

2. Establish breath pattern

Take a few moments to establish the basic 6-6 pattern you learned in Coherent Breathing™. Inhale for six seconds and exhale for six seconds. (Use the available audio, Coherent Breathing Symphony, if you like.)

3. Generate heart quality

Place your left hand over your heart and your right hand over it. Sense under your hands: notice your emotional state, how you feel. Notice how your breath and feelings are one and the same, just labels pasted, like sticky notes, over what is actually one thing. Let them be simply two currents within a single flowing stream. With each inhale, sense the heart quality expanding as the lungs expand, growing in volume and strength. Imagine your physical heart swelling like an inflating balloon. With each exhale, feel this energy condense into a concentrated ball deep in the center of your heart.

4. Direct the energy

Once you have created this pulsing ball of heart energy, direct it. Send it to someone you love. Imbue an object you value and appreciate with it. If your heart quality is compassion or loving-kindness, shower it on someone you know who needs it. Don't neglect to send it to yourself!

Follow-up Questions

- How exactly is my breathing now different from the last time I observed it?
- How does my breathing differ between different emotions and different levels of energy?
- How does thinking about something I feel grateful for affect my breathing?
- How does feeling pensive change it?
- How are different mental and emotional states reflected in my breathing pattern?

THIRTY-NINE

Centering The Storm (Fifty-To-Zen)

It was profound for me. Not only during it, but afterwards. I just sat there for another 10 minutes.

Yolanda

The biggest obstacle to meditation is thinking. How to stop the incessant flow of thoughts? Pay attention to your breath as it is occurring!

In the yoga tradition, this exercise is not considered meditation, much as *kapalabhati* is not considered a pranayama technique. Both are preliminary practices. Just as the physical practices of Hatha Yoga, the *asanas*, prepare one for breathwork (*pranayama*), the breathing practices prepare one for concentration (*dharana*). In turn, concentration practices prepare you for meditation (*dhyana*). The body/breath/mind sequence is explicitly laid out in what you may have heard called the *Eight Limbs of Yoga:*

- Yamas and Niyamas (ethics and morals)
- Asana (physical exercises and postures)
- Pranayama (breathing practices)
- Pratyahara (deep inquiry with sensory isolation)
- Dharana (concentrative techniques)
- Dhyana (meditation)
- Samadhi (realization, or insight)

Fifty-To-Zen is a *dharana* technique for strengthening focus and concentration. Only after zero does dharana transition to dhyana, or meditation. By the way, the word *Zen* is simply Japanese for *dharana*.

This technique comes from Erich Schiffman's book, *Yoga: The Spirit and Practice of Moving into Stillness.* Erich calls it, simply, *Counting Backwards.* The counting focuses your attention. Keeping up with the count forces you to pay attention, to not wander off. It gives your mind just enough of a challenge to keep it occupied. In meditation circles, this is known as *"throwing the dog a bone."*

Benefits

- The countdown gently concentrates your total awareness on the present moment, providing a way to de-stress simply by shifting your attention away from thoughts, worries, anxieties, and concerns.
- Cultivates mindfulness
- Strengthens concentration, the ability to shift from multi-tasking to uni-tasking at will

Preparations

Time, Set and Setting

Takes less than five minutes. Eliminate all environmental distractions so you will not be disturbed or distracted during the exercise.

Posture

Any posture will work as long as your spine is in anatomical neutral—so long as the spine is not bent, twisted, etc. I started to say so long as your spine is straight, but you might take the word literally. Unless specifically instructed otherwise, a straight spine means maintaining its four natural curves.

What to Watch For

You are not to control your breathing. It will slow down automatically. Simply focus on each half-breath as you count 50 to zero. This sequence sets the stage for the effortless meditation that follows.

It's expected that you'll get distracted at some point. Many times, more likely. Don't fret. Don't beat yourself up about it; to do so would heap more turbulence on top of what's already in your system! So, what should you do? Simply observe it, say something inwardly like, *Oh, my mind has wandered off. How interesting!* and, without further ado, patiently and gently bring your attention back to your right here, right now half-breath.

Practice Sequence

Quick Scan (Inquiry)

Assess your overall state. Take note of current conditions: thoughts, feelings, energy level, body sensations. Notice how your breathing reflects the overall situation both inside and outside your body. Notice everything.

Gradually narrow your attention onto just your breathing.

Before you start counting, take a few deep, slow breaths.

Take one more and begin on the next exhale...

Count backward from 50 to 20

- As you exhale, mentally and silently name it *"fifty"*
- As you inhale, mentally and silently name it *"forty-nine"*
- Exhale, *"forty-eight"*
- Inhale *"forty-seven"*
- Exhale *"forty-six"*
- Continue like this until you reach 20

Count only your exhales from 20 to 0

- Exhale *"twenty"*
- Inhale: listen to the sound and feel it but do not count it
- Exhale *"nineteen"*
- Inhale, but do not count it
- Exhale *"eighteen"*
- Inhale but do not count it
- Exhale *"seventeen"*
- [...]
- Exhale *"two"*
- Inhale
- Exhale *"one"*

- Inhale
- Exhale *"zero"*

Rest inside the Eye of the Storm!

Picture yourself inside the eye of the storm or a hurricane lantern: there is no wind to disturb your mind. The candle of attention does not flicker. Feel breathing, hear breathing. Bathe in the silence of thoughtlessness. You have arrived at zen! Linger here for at least a few breaths—better yet a few minutes. Enjoy the effects!

Follow-up

Notice the benefits of this short and simple exercise. You will likely feel refreshed, ready to emerge and return to activity feeling relaxed, able to focus, and ready to go about the rest of your day with renewed vigor.

FROM DREAMS AND ASPIRATIONS, HABITS OF MANIFESTATION

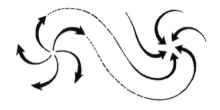

FORTY

Introduction To Part 6: The Challenge of Habits

When there is harmony between the mind, heart and resolution, nothing is impossible.[1]

Rig Veda

Habit mastery has always been important. Today more than ever. Tomorrow, habit mastery will be what separates those who thrive from those who merely breathe and occupy space. The practices included in this book have the potential to make a real difference in your life. Their long-term benefits are well worth the effort; a calm and relaxed body and mind are less prone to health issues. But you have to do them.

My former student, Elena, helped tremendously during the murky middle phase of writing this book. She was an invaluable sounding board and tireless supporter. Elena also inspires me with her dedication to practicing Coherent Breathing™ along with the Coherent Breathing Symphony audio tracks on *Insight*

Timer. Last time I checked, Elena had practiced over 600 days in a row!

Why is it so hard to make or break a habit?

Learning is the acquisition of knowledge through experience, study, or being taught. Learning is the process by which experience or practice results in a relatively permanent change in behavior or potential behavior.

Learning is what you must do when you want to respond differently the next time you encounter a certain stimulus, condition, or situation. To achieve this learning objective, you must create, modify, or extinguish a specific pattern of behavior in at least one of these categories: patterns of cognitive behavior (thinking, knowing); patterns of affective behavior (emotion, mood, feeling); or patterns of psychomotor behavior (doing, acting).

Our ability to learn is what sets us apart and makes us Earth's dominant species: learning is what molds the feral child into a cultured citizen, in the same way a gardener shapes a tree into an espalier. Learning is said to rely on the transfer of new information from perception to short-term and, most importantly, into long-term memory. If new content does not get encoded into long-term memory, it is soon forgotten.

Habits are a special class of learning. A habit is encoded into a much older region of the brain, the basal ganglia. Like a computer's ROM (Read-Only Memory), or a tattoo, habits can only be modified slowly or with difficulty. In fact, you can lose recall of your memories entirely and certain habits will go on just as before.

That's why learning, altering habits, and extinguishing habits is hard; the patterns imprint deeply, sometimes permanently, into the very fabric of the nervous system. When it allows you to multitask, such as drive and text and drink your morning coffee at the same time, it's great. But not if you're trying to stop smoking, drinking, or popping painkillers.

The tendency to pursue our goals with all-out zeal is normal and natural. It's also a surefire recipe for failure. It's also normal and natural to believe motivation and self-discipline will carry the day. If you want a new habit to stick, it's critically important to start with one or two small actions. If your goal is to quit smoking, for instance, and you decide to simply go cold turkey, to quit your two and a half pack a day addiction all at once, then you might as well not even start. I have known one or two people who have done just that, but they were the exceptions. I wish like hell I could have—it took me 15 years to quit smoking.

Many approaches to breaking bad habits employ a war mentality, one characterized by discipline. But approaching habit change from a battle mentality does not work in the long game. Consider the meaning of the word itself: approach literally means "move towards." That's why, as the saying goes, whatever you resist, persists. And that goes double with pernicious habits like smoking, gambling, drinking, and other physically or psychologically addictive behaviors.

New Year's Resolutions

Most New Year's resolutions don't last more than a few days or weeks because the motivation is not allowed enough time to gestate. When you think about the fact that agriculture was the pervasive concern for most of humanity back then, it makes perfect sense. There was little you could actually do until spring. And so, whatever you wanted to grow became rooted inside your mind. Its seed sprouted and grew in imagination over the course of the months when you were confined to the inside of your home. By the time you could take action, the motivation was strong and fully formed as a plan of action. And if you ran out of food, or ran out of the things you'd prefer to eat, your motivation grew correspondingly.

All I'm saying is if you want to make these practices a consistent and regular part of your daily life, it's essential to invest lavish amounts of time nursing your motivation!

The Secret Ingredient

Motivation comes from having a goal, aspiration, vision, or dream. In a word, desire. I desired better-looking teeth, so I spent thousands of dollars, money that was supposed to pay off a credit card, to have them whitened. I have not regretted my choice for a single day.

Failure in habit creation is not due to a lack of discipline. At least not in the usual sense of the word. My definition, again taken from one of my teachers, is this: discipline means remembering the original inspiration that caused you to make a commitment. The critical part is you have to remember it in moments of hesitation. Discipline revives the excitement you felt. It's the feeling that renews enthusiasm, not an iron will. The secret ingredient is to keep the flame for your desired future reality alive as if is already manifested.

Take Deepak Chopra as an example. In his book Overcoming Addictions, Deepak Chopra details his decades-long struggle to quit smoking. His story illustrates the critical role of positive motivation—inspiration—plays in creating and sustaining any new habit or routine. After years and years of trying to break his smoking habit, he succeeded only when he switched his tack. He stopped engaging in self-to-self combat and engaged instead in cultivating his desire for health and vitality:

I began smoking when I was 17 years old. Over the years I made many attempts to stop, but none were successful for long. I came to despise my smoking habit, and I was angry at myself for indulging in it. Very often I would furiously throw away the last five cigarettes in a pack while promising myself to quit. But within an hour or so I was furtively opening a new pack. I saw that in some way the cycle of self-reproach and guilt was a mechanism that kept my habit alive, but this insight had no practical effect on my smoking. I simply acted out the sequence again and again.

[…]

Then one evening I went to the ballet. As I sat there in the darkness admiring the graceful dancers, I could hear my own breathing coming in wheezes and gasps. The contrast made a powerful impression on me. Before me were superb athletes flying across the stage, and here I was struggling just to breathe.

The next day I was about to open a new pack of cigarettes, I felt more than my usual degree of guilt about my smoking. But I had learned by this time that guilt was not enough to break my addiction: in some mysterious way, guilt facilitated it.

So instead of combining the toxic experience of smoking with my own toxic self-reproach, I let my thoughts return to the beautiful dancers I had seen the night before. By doing so, I finally discovered the way to break the chain of my addictive behaviour, and I threw away my package of cigarettes.

Over the new few weeks, I called upon the memory of the dancers whenever I felt the desire to smoke. I gave up trying to fight my addiction, and instead replaced it with a positive alternative.[2]

Discipline is not a matter of doing what I said I would do despite no longer feeling like it. That works for a while, but at some point, I just get tired and give in. Discipline, for me, hinges on remembering the feeling of why I wanted to do it. In remembering why, the commitment is reaffirmed and I take the next action that leads in that direction rather than away from it.

What do you want? Do you desire health? Or to look good? Is it your heartfelt desire to have a full head of lustrous hair, a yoga butt, and six-pack abs. Would you like to have a gleaming Pepsodent smile?

FORTY-ONE

Birth Of A Nation's Habit

D o you brush your teeth three times a day, as everyone says you should? Or at least daily? I thought people always brushed. I assumed this tiny habit of brushing went way back, to the Greeks or the Romans or the Chinese. Or that a public health campaign got it over the tipping point, like with smoking. Instead, I discovered it was from this ad campaign for Pepsodent toothpaste in 1929:

One day in the early 1900s, a prominent American businessman named Claude C. Hopkins was approached by an old friend with an amazing new creation: a minty, frothy toothpaste named 'Pepsodent' that he promised was going to be huge. Hopkins, at the time, was one of the nation's most famous advertising executives. He was the ad man who had convinced Americans to buy Schlitz beer by boasting that the company cleaned their bottles 'with live

Pepsodent Ad (1929)

steam' (while neglecting to mention that every other company used the same method). He had seduced millions of women into purchasing Palmolive soap by proclaiming that Cleopatra had washed with it, despite the sputtering protests of outraged historians.

Hopkins' Pepsodent ads spawned the explosion of marketing based on the science of persuasion, according to Charles Duhigg, author of The Power of Habit:

> Today, Hopkins is almost totally forgotten. He shouldn't be. Hopkins was among the first to elucidate principles that even now influence how video games are designed, public health campaigns are managed and that explains why some people effortlessly exercise every morning, while others can't pass a box of doughnuts without automatically grabbing a jelly-filled cruller.[1]

Before Pepsodent, almost no Americans brushed their teeth. A decade after Hopkins' advertising campaigns, pollsters found that toothbrushing had become a daily ritual for more than half the population. Everyone from Shirley Temple to Clark Gable eventually bragged about a *Pepsodent smile*."

And the success of that one ad campaign launched the whole Mad Men ad men phenomenon.

I have a dream

This is my hope, my goal, my dream: one day in the near future breath-centered practices will be as commonplace as brushing. Children will be taught the techniques at a young age, both at home and at school. You will see people practicing in public—and no one will think them strange or weird. Employers will encourage 'breath breaks' because productivity, and therefore profit, will go up.

I want to be the one who is remembered as the 'Pepsodent Man' of breath-centered practices. But I'll be happy to see the campaign succeed even if I'm just another foot soldier who made a small contribution to the cause. To me, making a difference is what fulfills.

Many people will promise to turn you into a Black Belt Ninja Master of habits. But only I have the real secret (that's a joke, in case you didn't catch the sarcasm). Don't be surprised if you find creating, growing, and sustaining your new habit to be hard. I don't mean to make it sound impossible. It's not. All I am trying to tell you is that the process of habit formation takes more effort than the process of 'book learning.'

If you want the benefits that accrue from breath-centered practices, you already have the most essential ingredient. Aren't you glad you stayed the course and made it this far?

FORTY-TWO

The Tiny Habits Method

Plant a tiny seed in the right spot and it will grow without coaxing.[1]

In case you're thinking this is going to be hard, BJ Fogg has news for you. It's actually easy to instill a new habit. You just have to keep it simple and small. And you have to 'attach' the new, desired behavior to something you already do every day out of habit.

*Plant a tiny seed
(compound interest)*

A tiny habit is an action or behavior you perform at least once a day. It must not take a lot of time, energy, or effort. Four ingredients must occur at the same time in the same place for your Tiny Habit to work: aspiration, outcome, trigger, celebration. I'm confident that when you understand the Tiny Habits formula—how the four components work together to create a self-reinforcing habit loop—you'll see its utter beauty.

The Tiny Habits formula, to me, is the E=MC2 of habit creation.

Simple, Effective Habit Creation

This is the real deal. This method is not only evidence-based, but it is also the only one backed up by research. There is lots of 'social proof' as well. For example, here's what David Wallace, whose job description includes "work in policy, strategy, culture and behaviors, technology enablers, communities of practice, innovation, thought leadership, and change management," writes about the Tiny Habits method:

If you're at all interested in habit mastery, then you've likely encountered many experts who claim theirs is the best system for hacking the habit problem. What they do not provide is solid research evidence. The Tiny Habits Method is the only one backed up by solid evidence gathered from extensive research.

In his day job as director of Stanford University's Persuasive Technology Lab, BJ Fogg researches how to design computing products—from websites to mobile phone apps— that will have the most influence on behavior. I must admit, I was, initially, suspicious; I suspected that what BJ was up to was manipulative, perhaps even sinister.

But after watching his TEDTalk[2] from 2011, I knew BJ is more of a white-hat kinda guy. He's just not the nefarious, black-hat type. The research and design projects he's passionate about include technology for creating healthy habits, mobile persuasion, and physical activity.

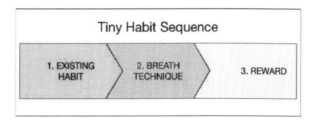

Tiny Habit Sequence

He also spends all day, every day—even while he sleeps—
working in his very own private laboratory: himself. Like the
TV ad says, "We live and breathe this stuff!" The first time I
watched it, I saw myself when I was eight, bursting with
questions. And playing my way to the answers.

In the TED Talk video, BJ shares one early experiment in the
evolution of The Tiny Habits Method. "This was the equation,"
he says into what is suddenly a laughter-filled auditorium:

I'm pretty sure that's not BJ doing the
pushup. I'm also pretty sure the hand
pressing the 'trigger' isn't his either. All
that matters is the Tiny Habits Method
he came up with in the end. And I
haven't found anything else that comes
close to its simplicity and that suits our
task as well.

*"After peeing, I will
do two push ups"*

FORTY-THREE

Design Your Habit

B y the power of compound interest, even one tiny new breathing habit, when repeated daily, can produce significant rewards.

If you want to enjoy the benefits breath-centered practices will produce—increased energy, focus, productivity, and better sleep, for instance, then you must practice them. It's not enough merely to read about them. But habits are perhaps the most difficult kind of learning. So it's

*Pot of Gold
(Compound Interest)*

no surprise that many of us find breaking bad habits and creating new ones challenging. That is why I urge you to start small. Rather than embarking on an ambitious program, the best way to get started is with the Tiny Habits Method. Just follow BJ Fogg's formula to create your new habit.

In this chapter you will design one new tiny breath-centered practice to incorporate into your day. You're going to practice it immediately following an existing behavior you already do every day. Soon you'll be telling everyone within earshot, this is easy!

A Lifestyle Habit Is Not A Project!

I caution you not to approach this as a project. Not the way you approach others. There are fundamental differences. Say you're working towards a deadline at work, one of those Friday close-of-business-day deadlines. You're responsible for a major project. Your actions must be linear and sequential. There can be only one moment you can celebrate, and that, of course, is when the project is 100% complete. You postpone anything and everything you can. You skip lunch and work extra hours. In short, you delay gratification.

Lifestyle habits don't work like that. Instead of delaying gratification until the entire goal has been accomplished, you design it into the habit itself. Instead of doing without and relying instead on motivation, willpower, and self-discipline, you reward yourself immediately. Every time you do the breath technique you reward yourself again. You'll want to do the new Tiny Habit not because it's a step closer to your aspiration but because of the instant payoff, the celebration. The more you do it, the greater the pleasure. Soon you'll forget all about getting to your desired future. You'll no longer be pursuing happiness because you're living it.

The technique you choose in this exercise will be your first step towards achieving your goals, your why. Who knows, it may turn out to be the first step of a lifelong journey!

Instructions

1. Choose The Trigger

Remember, this anchor is something you already do daily. Examples of existing behaviors to designate as your trigger:

- Brushing your teeth
- Walking to or from the bathroom
- Answering a phone call,
- Pressing the Return key after completing an email
- Turning a specific corner along your commute
- Switching a specific device on or off, such as your bedroom light
- Hearing the so-called sigh of satiation' that signals a full stomach

2. Choose A Breath Technique

Your new behavior must be limited to one you can accomplish in 30 seconds. Luckily, you can accomplish a lot within this time restraint! I have provided a number of techniques below that can be done in 30 seconds. Choose one from the list, use a question from the Inquiry exercise, or make up your own:

- For 30 seconds, just breathe! This is for you if you are among the many who stop breathing as an unconscious habit. If this is you, your task is simply to notice when and where you hold your breath and to use the holding as your trigger to start breathing again.
- Pay attention to – actually be with and experience – one half-breath at a time for 30-90 seconds. Say to yourself silently as you inhale, "*in-hale-this-half-breath*"; say to yourself silently as you exhale, "*ex-hale-this-half-breath*."
- Take 1 deep and slow inhale, hold it briefly, and let it fall out of your relaxed, slightly open mouth.
- Take one slow and deep diaphragmatic breath. If it

helps, count silently as you inhale to 4 or 6 or 8, then reverse the count as you exhale. For example: "one—two—three—four; four—three—two—one."

- While walking, count your steps (4-count or 6-count). Don't worry about synchronizing your breath and your steps at first. Get comfortable focusing mindfully on your steps. After a few repetitions, synchronizing breathing and walking will become the natural thing to do.

- Listen to the sound your breath is making for 30 seconds. Listen for the difference in pitch, volume, and timbre between the two.

- The Drop it Technique: I learned this ultra-simple instant stress relief technique from Dan Brule, author of *Shut Up and Breathe!* All you do is take one deep, slow inhale, hold it for just a moment, then let it fall out of your mouth with an exaggerated sigh. It should feel like dropping a ton of bricks off of your mind, heart, and body. I should probably warn you, though, that it's addictive. It feels so good you may find yourself repeating it many times a day. In fact, Brule recommends doing it 100 times a day!

- Calming 4-7-8 Breath. Inhale through your nose for four seconds; hold it in for seven seconds; exhale through your mouth for eight seconds. Keep your tongue touching the ridge above your upper front teeth as you exhale (or throughout the entire breath cycle). That's just 18 seconds! Truth be told, I won't send the yoga police on you if you do this twice, even though that will exceed your 30-second limit. Just don't tell BJ I approved it!

- For 30 seconds, stop whatever you're doing. Be still for half a minute and extend gratitude for breath, for life, or for anything you like.

- Honor satiation by stopping eating.

3. Decide How You'll Celebrate

Now add another sentence describing how you will celebrate your accomplishment. It should be something that feels good, that feels exactly as you would crossing the finish line of a marathon, reaching the peak of Mt. Everest, or whatever your 'moon mission' consists of. Again, I recommend watching BJ Fogg's TED Talk for inspiration; in it, he gets the audience to pump their fist in the air, Rocky-style, while saying "Awesome!"

Here are a few more examples of celebratory gestures:

- *That was easy!* (as you press the button in your mind)
- Spin around a time or two, stop, and say *That felt good!*
- *And here I thought I would have a hard time remembering or finding the time. I've got this!*
- Share your win. Tell your friends by sending a tweet, email, or by posting to social media.
- In your mind, drop a gold coin—endowed with the miraculous power of compound interest—into a magical piggy bank, like this one:

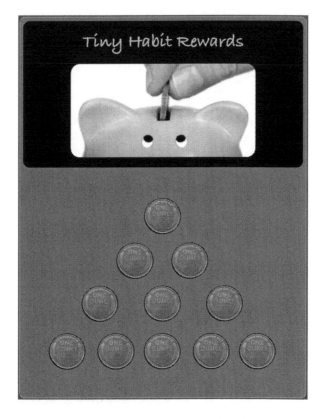

Tiny Habit Rewards (Piggy Bank)

FORTY-FOUR

Where Do You Catch The Bus For Tomorrow?

Jean Rubin is largely responsible for the fact that this book is not the book I set out to write. I have no idea if Jean is even still alive. But, like a few other teachers who have mattered in my life, Jean's voice lives on inside my head. If you are also a teacher, you may know how I feel when a former student tells you she or he still hears your voice. I can't think of a higher compliment–as long as what gets remembered is good.

So, here's what happened. About three or so months into writing this book, I heard Jean say, loud and clear, clear as a bell next to my ear, *Don't invite your reader to follow you around a corner you haven't even built yet!*

Frankly, those words never meant a whole lot to me before. But they made perfect sense on this day. What did it mean? Why did a write a different book? What was that first book, which will be my second book?

My original (next) book, "Cultivating Courage, Wisdom and

Serenity, One Half Breath At A Time." is structured around Arnold Niebhur's famous Serenity Prayer:

> *God grant me the serenity to accept the things I*
> *cannot change, the courage to change the*
> *things I can, and the wisdom to know the*
> *difference.*

On January 1, 2016–New Years Day–I was flipping through a friend's copy of *Yoga Therapy & Integrative Medicine: Where Ancient Science Meets Modern Medicine*[1]. Purely by accident, I found confirmation that I was not alone in recognizing a profound connection between breath-centered practices and the Serenity Prayer. In the section titled *"The Breathing Project,"* Leslie Kaminoff's words hit home like greased lightning:

> When encountering something over which we have no direct control, the only rational attitude is surrender. There is an anatomical basis for this teaching, and it is rooted in the nature of the breath. The human breathing mechanism operates in a delicate balance between voluntary and autonomic behavior. Anyone who has practiced pranayama as breath "control" knows how limited that control is!
>
> […]
>
> It's not surprising to me that thinkers as diverse as Patanjali [author of the Yoga Sutras] and Niebhur [author of the Serenity Prayer] came to the same conclusion: nature built these principles into the way life force courses through our bodies…[2]

The Serenity Prayer addresses us directly in critical moments of choice, when we must choose our future. It's these moments of doubt and uncertainty–and how we navigate them–that determine the course our lives take. Horace, the Roman poet, coined the term "dark night of the soul" to describe the pain and suffering, the mental fog and emotional friction, that accompanies these critical periods. Buddhists call it dukkha. And it's no accident we find ourselves tossed and turned by such tempests more and more frequently today, given the planet's growing volatility, uncertainty, complexity, and ambiguity (VUCA), as we discussed earlier in these pages.

I've been been through many disorienting dilemmas, those liminal spaces of upheaval that catalyze seismic shifts. Those forks in the road where you have to choose between different futures. When you have the chance to risk saying yes to what you know full well is a hazardous proposition. What's the difference between metamorphosis and transformation? What's the difference between, on one hand, metamorphosis–when a caterpillar changes into a butterfly, or a nymph into a dragonfly–and, on the other hand, transformation? Choice: insects have zero choice what to turn into. Each individual morphs into a more or less exact replica of every other individual of that species. They have no choice what to be when they grow up. They don't choose whether to become a Monarch or a Viceroy. Left turns are simply not available to them as they are for us. We have this curse/blessing: we can transform into something unprecedented if we have the courage to go for it.

And it may not work out.

But you also know, as Anais Nin pointed out, how life shrinks or expands in proportion to one's courage.

You have, haven't you?

If you're like me, the choosing part is way tougher than either accepting or changing. I can do acceptance. I also do change well. No, the hard part is knowing which option to choose in this situation–this relationship, this job. There is no ready formula, no algorithm, no *heuristic*, no rule-of-thumb we can use for the tough choices in life. The Serenity Prayer offers no concrete answers– except you should pray for wisdom. You're just going to have to make up your own mind and live with the consequences, whether good or bad, richer or poorer, whether it ends with the thrill of victory or the agony of failure.

Patanjali, on the other hand, does provide guidance, in the form of instruction in the path of Yoga. Whereas the Serenity Prayer provides instructions for contemplation when you're already standing at the fork in the road, the practices Patanjali offers prepare us far in advance. Likewise, the techniques I'm offering you, albeit invaluable at the crossroads, are really meant to be practiced proactively in order to arrive at each and every moment prepared.

Serenity Prayer for Breathwork

May I have the serenity to love this breath just the way it is.
May I have the courage to control my breath when to do so serves life.
May I have the wisdom to trust my own experience, my own knowing when choosing.

So, what about that "anatomical basis" Kaminoff alludes to? For that, you have to read the book and do the exercises. I'll give you one hint: it's the key that unlocks the treasure chest, so to speak; it's the mechanism that makes breathwork such a practical and powerful tool for anyone who lives and breathes, one breath at a time.

P.S. Presenting persuasive evidence for the power of breath-centered practices, partly through the anatomical basis, constitutes the 'corner' I needed to build first by publishing this book first. If you want to learn how to increase your serenity, courage, and wisdom with breath-centered practices, well then you'll just have to read the next book.

RESOURCES

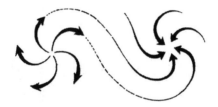

Online Resources

To claim your free guided practice audio, visit josephroberson.com/resources.

You can purchase the Coherent Breathing Symphony album (3 tracks) from my website (josephroberson.com/resources), CDbaby, or from Coherence.com.

Practice along with the Coherent Breathing Symphony audio for free on Insight Timer (https://insighttimer.com/yogajoe)

One Half-Breath At A Time Facebook Page (www.facebook.com/Breathing.One.Breath.At.A.Time/)

Breathing Community Facebook Group (www.facebook.com/groups/breathingcommunity)

Author website (www.josephroberson.com)

Twitter (twitter.com/yogajoe2u)

Instagram (instagram.com/joseph_r_roberson)

Notes

Prologue

1. Stephen Elliott is the originator of the Coherent Breathing method; the term, "Coherent Breathing," is a registered trademark of COHERENCE LLC.

Introduction

1. Weltman, G., Lamon, J., Freedy, E., & Chartrand, D. (2014). Police department personnel stress resilience training: an institutional case study. Global advances in health and medicine, 3(2), 72-9.

2. VUCA

1. -William Carlos Williams
2. Future Shock is a 1970 book by the futurists Alvin and Heidi Toffler in which the authors define the term "future shock" as a certain psychological state of individuals and entire societies. Their shortest definition for the term is a personal perception of "too much change in too short a period of time". The book, which became an international bestseller, grew out of an article "The Future as a Way of Life" in Horizon magazine, Summer 1965 issue.[2][3][4][5] The book has sold over 6 million copies and has been widely translated. (Wikipedia)

3. Dukkha

1. James Joyce, in Finnegan's Wake
2. Gilbert Ryle. The Concept of Mind. New York: Barnes and Noble; 1949.
3. https://psychcentral.com/lib/15-common-defense-mechanisms
4. https://psychcentral.com/lib/15-common-defense-mechanisms
5. Autumn Song, by Van Morrison

4. Distress

1. Hans Selye, *The Stress Response*.
2. Anna Katharina Schaffner, *Exhaustion: A History*

5. Chronic Stress

1. *Why Zebras Don't Get Ulcers* is a 1994 (2nd ed. 1998, 3rd ed. 2004) book by Stanford University biologist Robert M. Sapolsky. The book proclaims itself as a "Guide to Stress, Stress-Related Diseases, and Coping" on the front cover of its third and most recent edition. The title derives from Sapolsky's idea that for animals such as zebras, stress is generally episodic (e.g., running away from a lion), while for humans, stress is often chronic (e.g., worrying about losing your job). Therefore, many wild animals are less susceptible than humans to chronic stress-related disorders such as ulcers, hypertension, decreased neurogenesis and increased hippocampal neuronal atrophy. However, chronic stress occurs in some social primates (Sapolsky studies baboons) for individuals on the lower side of the social dominance hierarchy.

   Sapolsky focuses on the effects of glucocorticoids on the human body, stating that such hormones may be useful to animals in the wild escaping their predators, (see *Fight-or-flight response*) but the effects on humans, when secreted at high quantities or over long periods of time, are much less desirable. Sapolsky relates the history of endocrinology, how the field reacted at times of discovery, and how it has changed through the years. While most of the book focuses on the biological machinery of the body, the last chapter of the book focuses on self-help.

   Why Zebras Don't Get Ulcers explains how social phenomena such as child abuse and the chronic stress of poverty affect biological stress, leading to increased risk of disease and disability. (Wikipedia)

2. The term was conceived in the 1970s by African-American epidemiologist and public health researcher Sherman James while he was investigating racial health disparities between blacks and others in North Carolina.

   One of the people he interviewed was a black man, who, despite being born into an impoverished sharecropper family and having only a second grade education, could read and write. The man had freed himself and his offspring from the sharecropper system, had 75 acres of farmed land by age 40, but by his 50s, he had hypertension, arthritis, and severe peptic ulcer disease.

   His name, John Henry Martin, and his circumstances were evocative of folk hero John Henry, an African American who worked vigorously enough to compete successfully with a steam powered machine but died as a result of his effort. (SOURCE: https://en.wikipedia.org/wiki/John_Henryism)

3. *Exhaustion: A History*, by Anna Katharina Schaffner

6. Disease

1. The Institute for Science, Technology, and Public Policy's Congressional Prevention Coalition on Stress Prevention. Source: http://istpp.org/coalition/
2. Hippocratic Writings, by Geoffrey Ernest Richard Lloyd, John Chadwick, William Neville Mann (1978).

7. Dukkha Causes Disease

1. Ernesto L. Schiffrin, M.D., Ph.D., physician-in-chief at Sir Mortimer B. Davis-Jewish General Hospital, and professor and vice chair of research for the Department of Medicine at McGill University in Montreal. (Retrieved from www.heart.org on 2018-04-30)
2. Achim Peters, Bruce S. McEwen, Karl Friston. "Uncertainty and stress-Why it causes diseases and how it is mastered by the brain." 2017.

10. Curing Hypertension

1. The Institute for Science, Technology, and Public Policy's Congressional Prevention Coalition on Stress Prevention. Source: http://istpp.org/coalition/

11. Inspired By Example

1. Andrew Weil
2. mandibular tori: a bony growth in the jawbone along the surface nearest to the tongue.

12. Death by Unreasonable Panic

1. James Glennon, who trains police officers in the use of force, quoted in *Police officers across U.S. upset at being seen as brutal racists.* Lindsay Wise and Katy Moeller, 2014. McClatchy Washington Bureau.
2. Retrieved from: https://www.twincities.com/2017/12/16/one-year-on-prosecutor-discusses-cops-unreasonable-panic-in-castile-killing/
3. Retrieved from: https://www.twincities.com/2017/12/16/one-year-on-prosecutor-discusses-cops-unreasonable-panic-in-castile-killing/
4. Bill Johnson, executive director of the National Association of Police Organizations
5. James Glennon, who trains police officers in the use of force, quoted in

Police officers across U.S. upset at being seen as brutal racists. Lindsay Wise and Katy Moeller, 2014. McClatchy Washington Bureau.

6. McCraty, et al., 2012
7. Judith Andersen, 2016. Judith Andersen is a health psychologist whose research interests focus on the biopsychosocial mechanisms by which stress impacts mental and physical health. In addition to lab studies, she uses ambulatory psychophysiological equipment to conduct field research with people who experience trauma and severe stress. Prof. Andersen's on-going research projects include resilience training and research on the health and performance outcomes of psychophysiological stress intervention techniques for civilians, police and military personnel. SEE The HART (Health Adaptation Research on Trauma) Lab: https://hartlab.net
8. Lindsay Wise and Katy Moeller, 2014. "Police officers across U.S. upset at being seen as brutal racists." McClatchy Washington Bureau.

13. Chronic Emotional Distress

1. Phil Jackson, former head coach of LA Lakers and Chicago Bulls

14. Veterans with PTSD

1. Cholene Espinoza. Through the Eye of the Storm. 2006
2. Seppälä, E. M., Nitschke, J. B., Tudorascu, D. L., Hayes, A., Goldstein, M. R., Nguyen, D. T., Perlman, D., … Davidson, R. J. (2014). Breathing-based meditation decreases posttraumatic stress disorder symptoms in U.S. military veterans: a randomized controlled longitudinal study. Journal of traumatic stress, 27(4), 397-405.
3. Leslye Moore, National Director of Welcome Home Troops program. Private communication.

15. ACE of Hearts

1. Denise (pseudonym), private communication.
2. Gilbert, LK, Breiding, MJ, et al. "Childhood adversity and adult chronic disease: an update from ten states and the District of Columbia, 2010.
3. Dr. Nadine Burke Harris. The Deepest Well: Healing the Long-Term Effects of Childhood Adversity.
4. Denise (pseudonym), private communication.

16. Introduction to Part 3

1. 1 John Mayow, in Tractus Quinque, 1674. Quoted in Anatomy of Hatha Yoga, by Herbert David Coulter.

17. Why Breathe At All?

1. Source: https://www.verywellmind.com/carbon-monoxide-in-cigarette-smoke-2824730

19. The Respiratory Diaphragm

1. Boeckxstaens, G. E., 2005. *The lower oesophageal sphincter.* "The lower oesophageal sphincter (LOS) is a specialized segment of the circular muscle layer of the distal oesophagus, accounting for approximately 90% of the basal pressure at the oesophago-gastric junction. Together with the crural diaphragm, it functions as an antireflux barrier protecting the oesophagus from the caustic gastric content." (Retrieved from: https://www.ncbi.nlm. nih.gov/pubmed/15836451)
2. Karel F. Liem, 1988. Form and Function of Lungs: The Evolution of Air Breathing Mechanisms. Downloaded from https://academic.oup.-com/icb/article-abstract/28/2/739/211436
3. ibid

21. The Heart's Little Helper

1. Stephen Elliott, The New Science of Breath, pg. 18
2. The New Science of Breathing by Stephen Elliott, pg. 17

22. Bridge Over Troubled Wires

1. Sat Bir Singh Khalsa, PhD., Harvard researcher.

23. From Chaos to Coherence

1. Evalla, passenger on board JetBlue flight.
2. *Stress as a Precipitating Factor/Cause of Endocrine Disorders.* (Source: Ranabir, S., & Reetu, K. (2011). Stress and hormones. Indian journal of endocrinology and metabolism, 15(1), 18-22.)

24. Mindset (Words Matter!)

1. Oxford Dictionaries has declared "post-truth" as its 2016 international word of the year, reflecting what it called a "highly-charged" political 12 months. It is defined as an adjective relating to circumstances in which objective facts are less influential in shaping public opinion than emotional appeals. Nov 16, 2016. (Source: https://www.google.com/url?sa=t&rct=j&q=&esrc=s&source=web&cd=2&cad=rja&uact=8&ved=2ahUKEwi7v9rjlLTfAhVL2FkKHWc2ARkQFjABegQIBhAF&url=https%3A%2F%2Fwww.bbc.com%2Fnews%2Fuk-37995600&usg=AOvVaw0sRNzkK0_aMfw6HwgCaEPZ)

2. Zadra, J. R., and Clore, G. L. (2011). *Emotion and perception: the role of affective information.*

3. Respiratory sinus arrhythmia (RSA)—first described by Carl Ludwig more than 150 years ago (1)—is caused by phasic changes of vagal neural discharge directed to the sinus node. During inspiration, vagal activity is inhibited, causing a prompt heart rate increase. During expiration, the pattern of vagal discharge resumes, causing a prompt heart rate decrease 2, 3. Thus, the extent of the corresponding heart rate changes is largely dependent on vagal modulation.

   RSA is therefore a major determinant of heart rate variability (HRV), particularly when considering short-term HRV. RSA decrease is commonly observed in conditions characterized by altered sympathovagal balance with reduced vagal and increased sympathetic neural activity. In many clinical conditions (e.g., myocardial infarction [MI], heart failure), this autonomic pattern has been associated with a poor prognosis (4).

   Source: *Expiration-Triggered Sinus Arrhythmia Predicts Outcome in Survivors of Acute Myocardial Infarction*

4. Dr. Robert Fried, in *Breathe Well, Be Well.*

5. Federico Cortese, Music Director of the Boston Youth Symphony Orchestras and Senior Lecturer on Music and Director of the Harvard-Radcliffe Orchestra in the Department of Music at Harvard University

6. Dr. Robert Greenberg, American composer, pianist, musicologist.

25. Sympathetic Resonance

1. Feldman, J.L., Ellenberger, H.H., 1988. *Central coordination of respiratory and cardiovascular control in mammals.* Annual Review of Physiology 50, 593–606.

2. The New Science of Breath proposes a revolutionary theory of health based on autonomic nervous system balance - via breathing. Eastern cultures have held breathing in high esteem for thousands of years; references to its importance are to be found in some of civilization's earliest writings. Yet even today, while modern biological and medical sciences have made great strides in exploring and understanding the details of the human organism, including respiration at the cellular level, beyond gas exchange, the larger

biological function of breathing remains something of a mystery and is generally taken for granted. The New Science of Breath introduces Coherent Breathing, an exciting approach to health enhancement. It is based on the premise that while at rest the adult cardiopulmonary system, inclusive of autonomic nervous system aspects, resonates at a specific frequency, this frequency being essentially the same for all adults. When the breathing frequency is consciously aligned with this "reference rhythm" with appropriate depth, it results in optimal autonomic nervous system balance. Autonomic nervous system balance yields mental and physical comfort, a positive emotional outlook, enhanced health and well-being, and improved biometrics. (Source: Amazon)

26. Heart Rate Variability

1. Dr. Patricia Gerbarg and Dr. Richard Brown, The Healing Power of the Breath.

28. Inspired Yet?

1. Donna Farhi
2. Tony Briggs. "Breathing Lessons," Yoga Journal, November 2013
3. Erich Schiffman. Moving into Stillness: The Spirit & Practice of Yoga. P.3
4. Roger Cole

29. Your Wind Instrument

1. Erich Schiffman. Yoga: The Spirit & Practice of Moving Into Stillness.
2. Dr. Bruce Perry, How Your Brain Works 101

30. Getting Started

1. Hatha Yoga Pradipika, verse 2:15.
2. Kress, The Dark Side of Meditation, in Yoga Journal, May 2018. Retrieved from: https://www.yogajournal.com/meditation/the-dark-side-of-meditation-how-to-avoid-getting-stuck-with-pain-from-the-past)
3. ibid

31. The Gardener In The Garden

1. Rg Veda
2. The Synthesis of Yoga, Lotus Press, Twin Lakes, Wisconsin ISBN 0-941524-65-5

3. *The Synthesis of Yoga*, Lotus Press, Twin Lakes, Wisconsin ISBN 0-941524-65-5

4. "...the interconnected energy environment of shared information that surrounds us within cultures, communities, and our relationships with other people, and with the planet." (Source: https://www. imaginationmatters.org/index.php/2017/11/17/imagining-imagination/)

32. Begin

1. Erich Schiffman. *Yoga: The Spirit & Practice of Moving Into Stillness*.

33. Breath Inquiry

1. Breath Inquiry audio on Soundcloud:
        https://soundcloud.com/joseph-roberson-412250060/breath-inquiry-shy-2017-04-17

34. Easy Yoga For Breath

1. The ischial tuberosity (or tuberosity of the ischium, tuber ischiadicum), also known informally as the *sitz bone*, or as a pair the sitting bones) is a large swelling posteriorly on the superior ramus of the ischium. It marks the lateral boundary of the pelvic outlet. When sitting, the weight is frequently placed upon the ischial tuberosity. The gluteus maximus provides cover in the upright posture, but leaves it free in the seated position. (Wikipedia)

36. Coherent Breathing Symphony

1. https://insighttimer.com/yogajoe

40. Introduction To Part 6: The Challenge of Habits

1. Rg Veda
2. Deepak Chopra, Overcoming Addictions.

41. Birth Of A Nation's Habit

1. Charles Duhigg. *The Power of Habit*

42. The Tiny Habits Method

1. B.J. Fogg. *The Tiny Habits Method.*
2. https://www.youtube.com/watch?v=AdKUJxjn-R8

44. Where Do You Catch The Bus For Tomorrow?

1. *Yoga Therapy & Integrative Medicine: Where Ancient Science Meets Modern Medicine* by Ph.D., E-RYT500, YTRX, Larry Payne (Author), M.A., L.Ac., E-RYT500, YTRX, Terra Gold (Author), & 1 more.
2. Leslie Kaminoff. *Yoga Therapy & Integrative Medicine: Where Ancient Science Meets Modern Medicine.* On page 488, in the section titled *The Breathing Project.*

Acknowledgments

Editors

- Elena (Kim) Mawyer
- Qat Wanders
- Jessi (Rita) Hoffman

Contributors

- Elena (Kim) Mawyer
- Suzanne Dulin
- Stephen Elliott
- Denise (real name withheld)
- Ed Carlson
- Sandra K. Nicht

Teachers and Inspirers

- Erich Schiffman
- Donna Farhi
- Jessica Dibb
- Ravi Singh
- Kartar Singh Khalsa
- Shakta Kaur Khalsa
- Bodhi Ray
- Giten
- Maneesha James
- Tyohar
- Roger Cole
- Dan Siegel
- Joseph Cardarelli
- Jean Rubin
- James D. Dilts
- … and many more

Supporters and Cheerleaders

- Yolanda Hudspeth
- Lisa Gibbs Provence
- Stesha and Jeremy Warren
- Ty Ford
- Penny Williamson
- … and many, many more

Recommended Books, Articles, Audio

- *The New Science of Breath*, by Stephen Elliott

- *The Breathing Book*, by Donna Farhi
- *Yoga: The Spirit & Practice of Moving Into Stillness*, by Erich Schiffman
- *Breathing: The Master Key to Self Healing*, by Andrew Weil, M.D. (audio CD)
- *Breathe Well, Be Well*, by Dr. Robert Fried
- *Sensitive Chaos: The Creation of Flowing Forms in Water and Air*, by Theodor Schwenk
- *The Hidden Harmony: Talks on the Fragments of Heraclitus*, by Osho
- *Atmospheres of Breathing*, by Lenart Škof and Petri Berndtson (editors)
- *The Denial of Death*, by Ernest Becker
- *The Stress Response*, by Hans Selye
- … and many, many, many more!

About the Author

Joseph Roberson has been teaching yoga for 40 years and he's amazing at it. He's taught more than 5,000 classes. He has written, developed, managed, and led Yoga Teacher Teacher Training programs. He has created and conducted yoga retreats in the Mid-Atlantic region and in Costa Rica. He has a fascinating knowledge of breathwork. He's a brilliant photographer. He's an excellent writer. His passion is designing, creating, and implementing learning programs that transform learners deeply.

Suzanne Dulin, founder and owner of Sadhana Learning

About Joseph R. Roberson

(from the Amazon Author Page)

Joseph R. Roberson was born and raised in Rockingham County, North Carolina. His first job was picking tobacco. He took his second job as a library page to pay for his first international adventure: a five-week trip to England and Ireland between junior and senior years of high school. Since then, he has traveled to The Netherlands, Costa Rica, India, Thailand, Laos, and Myanmar. Along the way, he has earned Bachelor's and Master's degrees from the Maryland Institute of Art, plus a Master's degree in Instructional Systems Development. Roberson has taught art, papermaking, and breath-centered practices (yoga, pranayama, and meditation) to hundreds of students. His writing has appeared in numerous publications, including Hand Papermaking Magazine, The Poetry of Yoga, The Art of Wellbeing, Chiang Mai Guidelines, and Chiang Mai City Paper. His art has been featured in exhibits such as: Six Directions in Paper (a traveling exhibit Roberson curated), The Mythic Vision, and a one person show at Chiang Mai University.

Made in the USA
Monee, IL
24 February 2021

61231892R00173